God and Science

A Quest for Christian Credibility

Arthur Peacocke

God and Science

A Quest for Christian Credibility

SCM PRESS LTD

The cover photograph shows the first model of DNA
made with space-filling representations of its constituent
atoms at the Biophysics Laboratory of King's College,
London and published in 'The Nuclear Basis of Heredity'
by W. G. Overend and A. R. Peacocke in *Endeavour* vol. 16,
1957, p. 98.

0 334 02673 3

First published in Britain 1996
by SCM Press Ltd
9–17 St Albans Place, London N1 0NX

Typeset by Regent Typesetting, London
and printed in Great Britain by
Biddles Ltd, Guildford and King's Lynn

Contents

To the thinking church
and for
the beginning of the millennium

Preface

Although science had for many centuries – not least during its creative flowering in the seventeenth – a mutually enhancing dialogue with the Christian religion, our present century has nurtured a public image of science as materialistic, reductionist and, for some prominent expositors, atheistic. It is therefore not surprising that educated people imprinted with this image, have found the beliefs of the Christian faith, in their received and traditional forms, to be less and less believable and often downright untrue. Yet the expansion of human horizons which is stimulated by the increasingly comprehensive vista of the sciences from cosmology to ecology ought rather to have provided an opportunity for the enrichment of Christian thought.

For the scientific panorama of the evolution of the cosmos from matter-energy into life and consciousness should surely afford a new and fruitful context for understanding any genuinely true insights that the Christian tradition might claim to possess. Inevitably the new perspectives of science challenge Christians to re-think the meaning and mode of expression of their insights. The process can be painful as well as invigorating but its aim must be to shape and formulate our understandings of nature, humanity and God – and of the particular role of the Jesus of history and the Christ of faith – so that they are actually credible in this last decade of the twentieth century, the prelude to the next millennium.

There are many in our society who are 'cultural despisers' of the Christian faith but there are also, more numerous I believe, many wistful agnostics who would like to find a way with intellectual integrity of appropriating Christian insights in our spiritually impoverished times – and there are perhaps even more who are simply ignorant and need to hear that faith anew in a believable form. This book, based on lectures given to the South African Science and Religion Forum in 1995 and on my earlier Gifford Lectures at St Andrews University, is directed to all of these groups, especially the last two – and perhaps even the first might be prepared to think again. Its approach is not so much 'faith seeking understanding', as so much Christian writing on religion and science turns out to be, but rather 'understanding seeking faith'. It also assumes that in public discourse both understanding and faith must proceed in their development by the application of the normal criteria for reason-ableness in order to command general assent.

Certainty is rarely vouchsafed to limited human intellects in such a quest and probability still is 'the very guide to life', as the redoubtable Joseph Butler affirmed long ago. Nevertheless, an attempt is made here to encompass in one framework and vision what we know of nature, humanity and God and thereby to point to the Christian 'Way' as worthy of the assent of, at least, our minds – and eventually, and more demandingly – of our-selves.

I

Nature and God

Anyone who reads Dante's *Divine Comedy*, whether in the original, if so capable, or in one of the many fine translations, cannot but be enormously impressed by the sheer synthetic power of his poetic imagination in integrating into one compelling narrative the cosmological, philosophical and theological insights of his times (1265–1321). Its astronomy is extraordinarily up-to-date for its time and its philosophy sophisticated. Furthermore its theology is the fruit of a lifetime's study and pilgrimage, for it begins (Sayers 1949: 71) memorably in that 'dark wood' of the frustrations, despair and dereliction of his middle years:

> Midway this way of life we're bound upon
>> I woke to find myself in a dark wood,
>> Where the right way was wholly lost and gone.

In the confusions and loss of hope of our present times we know only too well what he means. But in the story, Dante is led by the figure of Virgil, the embodiment of Human Wisdom, to the very threshold of Heaven through which he is guided by Beatrice, the representative of all those agencies which have become for humanity 'the God-bearing image, the revelation of the presence of God' (Sayers 1949: 68). She finally leads him to that sublime ultimate vision of the mystery of the divine, the way to which has been the underlying theme of the whole allegory (Sayers and Reynolds 1962: 347):

High phantasy lost power and here broke off;
   Yet, as a wheel moves smoothly, free from jars,
   My will and my desire were turned by love,
The love that moves the sun and the other stars.

For most of us moderns, including post-moderns, this is a vision for which we may well yearn but do not expect to be consummated. For that human wisdom, which was personified by Virgil, no longer leads us so clearly and unambiguously to the threshold of the divine.

The process of disruption of this unitary vision was beginning to be discerned later when John Donne, the English divine and poet, writing in 1611 three centuries after Dante and half a century or so after Copernicus' *De Revolutionibus*, could expound his *Anatomie of the World (The First Anniversary)* thus:

And new philosophy calls all in doubt,
     . . .
Tis all in pieces, all cohaerence gone;
All just supply, and all Relation.

Here we sense something of that anguish which was experienced with the breakdown under pressure from the 'new philosophy' (what we call 'science') of the mediaeval perception of a divinely-ordered and hierarchically organized cosmos in which humanity had an intermediate but highly significant location as a bridge between the earthly and the heavenly. We hear an echo of the desolation that was felt at the loss of an awareness of organic unity – 'Tis all in pieces' – of a divine placement for humanity, and indeed of all things living and non-living, in an organic whole.

The relation between science and religion today

But neither scripture nor the poets could, after the seventeenth century, stem the rising tide of an individualism in which the self surveyed the world as subject over against object. This way of viewing the world involved a process of abstraction in which the entities and processes of the world were broken down into their constituent units. It may be depicted, somewhat over-succinctly, as the asking of 'What's there?'; then, 'What are the relations between what is there?'; and, the ultimate objective of science, 'What are the laws describing these relations?' To implement this aim a reductionist method – the breaking of things into their constituent parts – was often essential. Thus it was that the natural world came to be described as a world of entities involved in law-like relations which determined the course of events in time.

The staggering success of these procedures cannot be over-estimated. In the course of three hundred years they have altered the whole perspective of Western humanity. It is the impact of this revolution on religious belief in general and, more particularly, on Christianity which has made its credibility an urgent issue for this last decade of the twentieth century. For I agree with Clifford Longley when he wrote in *The Times* of 15 February 1988, in an article concerned with how the decline of morality stems from a decline in belief in the Christian faith, 'What most characterizes the decline of faith in Britain is the perceived loss of credibility of religious belief, because it seems to have no foothold in a philosophical world view where the whole of reality can be encompassed by science.'

The history of the relation between science and religion will not be pursued here. Suffice it to say that this history displays a complexity and variety of interrelationships between those two great human concerns which totally belies any simplistic description of it as one of 'conflict', the label so beloved of the media. For the media still propagate, almost unconsciously, a 'warfare' model of the relation of science and religion, as evidenced every time the British Association for the Advancement of Science meets. Then there unfailingly appear gleeful, and historically inaccurate (see Lucas 1979), accounts of the encounter at its 1860 meeting between T. H. Huxley and the then Bishop of Oxford, Samuel Wilberforce. To this day it is still not regarded as quite professionally respectable for a biologist to admit to being a Christian. For, example, there was, even in 1992, the spectacle of a contemporary biologist, Richard Dawkins, taking the role of a Huxley-*redivivus* in attempting scornfully to denounce religion represented by the then Archbishop of York, Dr John Habgood. The occasion was the Edinburgh International Festival of Science and it was intriguing to observe the anti-religious and biassed reporting it received from the science correspondents even of the broadsheets. This provoked articles and counter-articles, letters and comments in all the media – all good rollicking stuff, showing that 'science *versus* religion' was still regarded as a newsworthy sport.

Our concern here is with the proper state of their relationship. For it is as true today as it was some sixty years ago that, as A. N. Whitehead (quoted in Brooke 1991: 1), the mathematician-philosopher, then affirmed, 'the future course of history would depend on the decision of his generation as to the proper relations between science and religion – so powerful were the religious symbols through which men and women conferred meaning on their lives, and so powerful the scientific models through which they could manipulate their environment'. The reports of the debate between Richard Dawkins and the Archbishop demonstrated that different perspectives were operating in the arguments concerning the actual status of scientific and religious affirmations and what counts as evidence for them. Indeed one of the most telling points in Dr Habgood's trenchant response to Dawkins, when he had at last a chance to operate on a level playing field in the columns of *The Independent* (5 March 1992), was that 'teasing out the relationship between these

different kinds of knowledge, and exposing the fatal consequences of a lopsided concentration on only one kind, is a task
for philosophy'. A vital aspect of the relation of science to
religion is indeed to sort out how they differ with respect to the
kind of knowing they each represent – and this is as much a
challenge to science as it is to religion.

In a post-modern age science itself has come under attack as
being sociologically and ideologically conditioned, even with
respect to its actual content – the knowledge it asserts it has
of the world. Religion, of course, has long had to suffer such
attacks and the impugning of its claimed knowledge of God
and humanity. The disputes are about the significance to
be attributed to the language employed in these only too-human
activities. Let me now give my viewpoint on these vexed
issues, for such clarification is essential as a prelude to what
follows.

Briefly, I think that both science and theology *aim* to depict
reality; that they both do so in metaphorical language with the
use of models; and that their metaphors and models are revisable
within the context of the continuous communities which have
generated them. This philosophy of *science* ('critical realism') has
the virtue of being the implicit, though often not articulated,
working philosophy of practising scientists who aim to depict
reality but know only too well their fallibility in doing so. A
formidable case for such a critical scientific realism has
(McMullin 1984: 30) been mounted based on the histories of, for
example, geology, cell biology and chemistry, which during the
last two centuries have progressively and continuously dis-
covered hidden structures in the entities of the natural world
that account causally for observed phenomena. Models and
metaphors are in fact widely used in science but this does not
detract from the aim of such language to refer to realities while
it does entail that these models and metaphors are always in
principle revisable.

Theology, the intellectual formulation of religious experience and beliefs, also employs models which may be similarly described. I urge that a critical realism is also the most appropriate and adequate philosophy concerning religious language and theological propositions. Theological concepts and models should be regarded as partial, inadequate, and revisable but necessary and, indeed, the only ways of referring to the reality that is named as 'God' and to God's relation with humanity. Models and metaphor obviously play an even wider role in religious language than in science. In theology, we also have to attempt *to infer to the best explanation* by application of the normal criteria of reasonableness: fit with the data, internal coherence, comprehensiveness, fruitfulness and general cogency.

In this perspective both science and theology are engaging with realities that may be referred to and it is therefore entirely appropriate to ask how what scientists believe about the natural world and religious people believe about God and nature, including human nature, should be related. Science and theology certainly always have been interrelated in the history of both of them, with the boundary lines demarcating them continuously shifting. Moreover, on theology's own presuppositions, if God's own self has given the world the kind of being and becoming it has, then it must in some respects reveal God's nature and purposes. So theology should seek to be at least *consonant* with those scientific perspectives on the natural world that are well-established, as far as can be reasonably judged – for it is notorious that a theology which *marries* the science of today runs the risk of becoming a widow tomorrow!

This chapter began by referring to Dante's unified vision of nature, humanity and God. What is the vista that twentieth-century science now unveils for our contemplation?

The world of science

We live in a world that, extrapolating backwards in our clock-time, may be said to have 'begun' some ten to fifteen billion (thousand million) years ago in, according to some currrent speculations, the fluctuation of what is called a 'quantum field'. What is reasonably clear is that in an almost inconceivably small interval of time an unimaginably condensed mass of fundamental particles and quanta of energy came into existence which has, over millions of years, coalesced in an expanding space into the present observable universe – with its billion galaxies each containing between a hundred and a hundred thousand million stars. On one particular planet (our Earth) circulating one of these stars (our Sun) in one of these galaxies, conditions were such as to allow the formation of more and more complex molecules from the atoms it had inherited from some supernovae explosion aeons before. By their inherent properties systems of molecules came into existence that could copy their own patterns of organization – matter became living. The living forms expanded by the incorporation into their systems of other molecules and in doing so competed with each other for limited resources – the evolution of living organisms by natural selection was under way. The advantages it conferred stimulated an increase in complexity as time proceeded. The history of the cosmos and of life on the Earth indeed manifests an emergent quality. For the concepts which are hammered out by the sciences appropriate to each level of complexity cannot be reduced to those that apply to their constituents. So genuinely new kinds of reality appear in the evolutionary process which can rightly therefore be called 'creative'.

In natural selection, it is an advantage for a living organism to be able to process information received from the environment, including any predators, so as to be able to adjust to its challenges. Hence the development of sensitive monitoring and information-storing systems – in fact, senses, nerves and brains – was an inbuilt propensity of the process. Such advantages could be further compounded by social communication and organization: thus language, and with that forms of consciousness, emerged under pressures of natural selection in those

creatures capable of such information retrieval. These propensities – towards complexity, information-processing and consciousness – eventually coalesced in the uniquely concentrated
form of the personal self-consciousness of *homo sapiens*. Such is
the interplay of chance and law in the evolutionary process that
(be it noted) these propensities might have been embodied in a
quite different physical form – our possessing five digits on each
of four limbs, for example, is sheer happenstance. Thus the
original fluctuation in a 'quantum field' has come to take the
form of human persons with all their creativity and diversity.
The dust of the cosmos has become a Mozart, a Shakespeare,
Jesus of Nazareth – all of us! What might a latter-day twentieth-
century Dante make of that!

There are two particular aspects of our scientific understanding of the world which have really only come to the fore during
the last decade or so, which are not yet widely appreciated by
theologians and which are possibly significant for developing an
intelligible and believable way of conceiving of God's relation to
the world.

One of the striking developments in science in recent years
has been the increasing recognition that many dynamical
systems – physical, chemical, biological and indeed neurological
– that are governed by non-linear dynamical equations can
become *unpredictable* for us in their macroscopically observable
behaviour. Examples of such (so-called 'chaotic') time-depen-
dence include: turbulent flow in liquids; predator-prey patterns;
stirred reactor systems that involve autocatalytic relations;
yearly variation in insect and other populations in nature; and, to
no one's surprise, the weather (cf., the famous 'butterfly effect').

It is now realized that the time-sequence of such complex
dynamical systems can take many forms: 'limit cycles', regular
oscillations, systems that 'flip' between these two alternative
allowed states, etc. It is important to stress that in these
cases this unpredictability is an ineradicable one. It is truly
unpredictable *for us* – we will never have sufficiently accurate

knowledge of the conditions prevailing during the fluctuations (especially if it proves necessary to take quantum events into account) to predict indefinitely which way the system will go. There is a 'predictability horizon'.

In the real world most systems do not conserve energy: they are usually open, *dissipative systems* through which energy and matter flow. Such systems can often give rise to the kind of sequence just mentioned and often exhibit a change-over to temporal and spatial patterns in the system, what Ilya Prigogine and his colleagues at Brussels have called 'order through fluctuations' (see, among others, Prigogine 1980; Prigogine and Stengers 1984; Peacocke, 1983: ch. 2). In such systems, matter displays an ability to be self-organizing and self-making, thereby bringing into existence new forms entirely by the operation of forces and the manifestation of properties we already understand. 'Through amplification of small fluctuations it [nature] can provide natural systems with access to novelty' (Crutchfield and others 1986: 48).

But there is another aspect of complex systems in nature which must also be recognized. This is the long-neglected phenomenon which has been, clumsily and variously, called 'downward-' or 'top-down' 'causation' (Campbell 1974: 179–186; Sperry 1983: ch. 6) or, better in my view, 'whole–part constraint'. The notion of causality, when applied to systems, has usually been assumed to be 'bottom-up' the effect on the system of the properties and behaviour of its constituent units. However, in the case of these systems there has also to be recognized an influence of the state of the system *as a whole* on the behaviour of its components, a constraint exercised by the whole on its parts. In such instances (e.g., the interplay between evolved DNA sequences and a creature's environment; the vertical convection in a liquid heated from below), the changes at the lower level of the constituent units, are what they are because of their being part of that particular system, which is exerting *as a whole* specific constraints on its units, making them behave otherwise than they would if in isolation. Yet these units still observe the regularities, that is obey the laws, observed by the sciences pertinent to them at their own level.

Description of such complex interlocking networks of events and changes operating at different levels does not seem adequately to be captured by their description as 'causally' connected, with its often hidden assumption that some kind of force is at work. There seems rather to be here a determination of form through *a flow of information*, rather than through a transmission of energy where 'information' is conceived of in a broad enough sense to include not only the communication engineer's sense but also its wider connotation in the sense of 'that which gives form to'. Such determinative relations of form by form may operate between two different kinds of 'level' of complexity in nature and require a flow of information between them.

It is in terms such as these that some neuro-scientists and philosophers have also come to speak of the relation between mental events and the physico-chemical changes at neurones, which are the triggers of observable actions in those living organisms that possess brains sufficiently developed that it is appropriate to attribute to them some kind of consciousness. For Roger Sperry, for example, 'mental events' in human beings are the internal descriptions we offer of an actual total state of the brain, such a brain state acting as a constraint on what happens at the more micro-level of the individual neurones. What occurs at this 'lower' level is what it is because of the prevailing state of the whole. There is operative here a whole-part constraint between the level of the brain state as a whole and that of the individual neurones. This process is again probably best conceived of in terms of the transfer of information rather than of energy, in the way a program representing a certain equation, say, controls the chips in a computer – but we must remember that this whole area of investigation is still very much *sub judice*.

In the foregoing, a deliberately broad brush has been used,

emphasizing only some pertinent features of the present scientific vista. It must now be asked, if science is indeed depicting the realities of nature, what are its implications for our understanding of that reality which theology attempts to depict? Recall that that reality – depicted in models and by metaphors – is the 'God' who is experienced in the monotheistic traditions as rendering intelligible and coherent the very existence of the natural world. This is the natural world whose entities, structures and processes the sciences refer to in *their* models and metaphors. The humanity which has come into existence through its seamless web of natural processes seeks urgently, and even passionately, for the meaning of its own existence and of that from which and within which it has emerged. This long search for meaning is the religious quest of humanity and cannot but be affected by this new perspective from the sciences of where we have come from and the processes that have enabled us to be here at all.

God

It is necessary, therefore, to ask to what extent the concepts, models and images of God that have been winnowed and refined, particularly in the Judaeo–Christian tradition, can be illuminated by those impressive, at times mind-boggling, perspectives on the world that the natural sciences now give us.

Our sense of the sheer apparent 'givenness' of the world – of its obstinate contingency and actuality – is enhanced by our current awareness of the scientific vista just outlined. Even the 'quantum field', fluctuations in which are postulated as having initiated the expansion of the present observed universe, is not, strictly speaking, simply 'nothing at all'. *Its* existence still calls for explanation of some kind, in the sense that it need not have existed at all. Indeed the quantum, gravitational and relativity laws themselves could have been otherwise, so the contingency will persist even if cosmologists begin to find other ways of describing the origin of our expanding universe. Hence the postulate of the existence of some 'Ground of Being' continues to be plausible as an answer to that most basic of all questions, 'Why is there anything at all?'

From the scientific perspective, the world exhibits an underlying unity – which may eventually be concentrated into only a few, or even one, equation (the famous 'TOE', 'Theory Of Everything') – yet it also manifests a remarkable diversity, fecundity and multiple levels of complexity. The sought-for 'best explanation' of such a world's existence and character and, if any is to be found at all, it cannot but be grounded in One unifying source of creation and inbuilt creativity, which must also possess a mode of Being of unfathomable richness, multiple in expression and outreach.

Everything that scientific research dis-covers shows a world that is more and more expressible in a rational and intelligible accounts – it is found to possess an inherent, inbuilt rationality. As Hoyle (1960: 103) once remarked: 'When by patient enquiry we learn the answer to any problem, we always find, both as a whole and in detail, that the answer thus revealed is finer in concept and in design than anything we could ever have arrived at by means of a random guess.' The Ground of Being of such a world must be supremely rational.

The natural sciences have moreover, since Einstein, led us to understand that time is a relationship within the natural order, and is closely integrated in his Relativity Theory with space, matter and energy. So theists must regard time as 'created', as being given existence by God and as an aspect of the created nexus of events. Moreover, in the macroscopic world, time has a direction, in which there emerge new entities, structures and processes. This reinforces the notion that the Ground of our Being is the Sustainer and faithful Preserver through time of all-that-is and of all-that-is-becoming.

'Ground of Being, One, of unfathomable richness, supremely rational, Sustainer and faithful Preserver' – this humanity calls

'God', as St Thomas Aquinas would have said today, and we will follow his usage.

The scientific perspective is of a *dynamic* world of entities and structures. New realities come into being, and old ones often pass away, so that God's action as Creator is both past and present and future – it is continuous and in the very process itself. This entails a new emphasis into what is called God's 'immanence' in, God's presence to, the world that God is continuously creating. God is the Immanent Creator, acting in and through the creative processes of the natural order, revealed by the sciences.

The notion that God gives existence to something other than Godself, that all-that-is has a derived and dependent being and becoming, is implied in the attribution to God of 'transcendence'. In order to express this, theists have found themselves culturally conditioned to say that the transcendent Creator gives existence to the world as other than, and so 'outside' *him*self. At this point particularly, the patriarchal forms of speech we have inherited prove to be quite inadequate, indeed downright misleading. For God is the One in whom 'we live and move and have our being' (Acts 17.28 AV), so that the world is 'in' God, but not 'of' God (pan-*en*-theism), in the sense of being identical with God – the world has its own distinctive kind of being. Because it is women who experience the carrying of new life within them, it would be more appropriate also to say that God creates the world within *her*self, if we are (inevitably misleadingly) to use personal language and gender-definite personal pronouns of God at all.

The scientific 'anthropic principle' affirms that the world is finely tuned with respect to many physical features in a way conducive to the emergence of carbon-based life and so of human beings. The presence of humanity in this universe, far from being unintelligible, represents an inherent in-built potentiality of that physical universe in the sense that intelligent, self-conscious life was bound eventually to appear – somewhere, some time – although its *physical* form was not prescribed by those same fundamental quantities and relationships that made it possible. Does not the very intimacy of our human relation to the fundamental features of the physical world, its 'anthropic' features, together with the irreducible distinctiveness of person-hood, point us in the direction of looking for a 'best explanation' of all-that-is in terms of some kind of entity that could *include* the personal? Hence we have good reason for saying that God is (at least) 'personal', or 'supra-personal' and for predicating personal qualities of God as less misleading and more appropriate than impersonal ones. But even as we say this, we have to recognize that personal attributes alone will never exhaust the nature of that ineffable Reality which is God who is always going to be intrinsically more than we can ever in principle conceive.

The natural world is immensely variegated in its hierarchies of levels of entities, structures and processes, in its 'being'; and abundantly diversifies with a cornucopian fecundity in its 'becoming' in time. From the unity in this diversity and the richness of the world there were adduced above both the essential oneness of its source of being, namely the one God the Creator, and the unfathomable richness of the unitive Being of that Creator God. But now the diversity itself needs to be emphasized more strongly. As Charles Darwin himself put it in the famous concluding passage of *The Origin of Species*,

It is interesting to contemplate a tangled bank, clothed with many plants of many kinds, with birds singing on the bushes, with various insects flitting about, and with worms crawling through the damp earth, and to reflect that these elaborately constructed forms, so different from each other, and dependent upon each other in so complex a manner, have all been produced by laws acting around us . . . There is grandeur in this view of life, with its several powers, having been originally breathed by the Creator into a few forms or into one; and that, whilst this planet has gone cycling on according to the fixed law of gravity, from so simple a beginning endless forms most beautiful and most wonderful have been, and are being evolved.

The existence of the *whole* tapestry of the created order, in its warp and woof, and in the very heterogeneity and multiplicity of its forms must be taken to be the Creator's intention. Sense can only be made of that, utilizing the resources of personal language, if God may be said to have something akin to 'joy' and 'delight' in the fecundity of creation. A hint of this idea of the satisfaction attributed to God as Creator already appears in the first chapter of Genesis (1.31): 'And God saw everything he had made, and behold, it was very good.' It leads naturally to the idea of the 'play' of God in creation which appears also in Hindu thought and in that of Judaism (in the 'Wisdom' literature) – daring to say that God has joy and delight in creation.

The investigations of the Brussels school, under Ilya Prigogine, and of the Göttingen school, under Manfred Eigen (Eigen and Winkler 1981), have demonstrated that it is the interplay of chance and law that is in fact creative within time, for it is the combination of the two which allows new forms to emerge and evolve – so natural selection appears to us as opportunistic. The principles of natural selection involve the interplay and consequences of random processes (in relation to biological outcome) in the lawlike framework of the rules governing change in biological populations in complex environments. This, for a theist, now has to be regarded as an aspect of the God-endowed features of the world.

Hence, the theist might say, since the potential of the 'being' of the world is made manifest in the 'becoming' that the operation of chance makes actual, that God is the ultimate ground and source of both law ('necessity') and 'chance'. On this view God acts to create in the world *through* what we call 'chance' operating within the created order, each stage of which constitutes the launching pad for the next. However, the actual course of this unfolding of the hidden potentialities of the world is not a once-for-all pre-determined path, for there are inherent unpredictabilities in the actual systems and processes of the world (quantum micro-events at the 'Heisenberg level' and human free will). This leads us to suggest that God the Creator explores in creation, making its vast potential actual.

Considerations such as these impel a recognition, more emphatically than ever before, of the constraints which God must be conceived of as imposing upon God's own self in creation and to assert that God has, as it were, 'self-limited' the scope of operation of God's own omnipotence and omniscience. There are certain areas over which God has chosen not to have power, for example in endowing humanity with free will, as traditionally recognized. God has chosen *not* to know what we will do, say, at a certain time tomorrow by creating us, via the processes of evolution, with free will. The attribution of 'self-limitation' to God in regard to God's omniscience is also meant to suggest that God may also have so made the world that, at any given time, there are certain systems (quantum ones) whose future states cannot be known with complete precision even to God. For there are no facts of the matter about their future states *for* God to know, so God cannot know them. 'Omniscience' as an attribute of God means that God knows all and whatever it is logically possible to know.

All of which has another consequence – it is that this unpredictability and open-endedness of much that goes on in the world, especially in the actions of free-willing humanity, means that it is appropriate to say God 'took a risk' in creation – that God allowed Godself to be vulnerable to what the emergent entities in creation might do or become. God, this implies, takes a risk to achieve some overriding purpose, which must include the creation of responsible, free persons.

But the whole process involves the pain, suffering and death of living organisms and if we take seriously that all this occurs, in some sense, as 'in God', that God is the One 'in whom we live and move and have our being', that God is immanently present 'in, with and under' these processes. Furthermore, if God is to be regarded as not indifferent to the suffering in the world, that God is not a moral enormity making us mere playthings of an absentee deity; then it is necessary to affirm that God suffers in, with and under the creative processes of the world with their costly, open-ended unfolding in time. (Christians, of course, have other compelling reasons for affirming this, as we shall consider later.)

With such conceptions of God in mind resulting from our reflections on some implications of the scientific perspectives on the world, the question arises naturally of how we are to conceive of

God's interaction with the world

Unpredictability The world is notably less predictable than has been the presupposition of much theological reflection on God's action in the world since Newton. It is observed to possess a degree of openness and flexibility within a law-like framework, so that certain developments are, and will continue to be, inherently unpredictable *by us* on the basis of any conceivable science.

The history of the relation between the natural sciences and the Christian religion affords many instances of gaps in causal explanations, that is, instances of unpredictability, being unwisely exploited by theists as evidence of the presence and activity of God whose direct action is postulated as filling them. But now we have to reckon with a new *inherent* kind of unpredictability in certain sequences of events – that is, *permanent* gaps in our ability to predict events in the natural world. Does this imply a 'God of the *unclosable* gaps'? There would then be no fear of such a God being squeezed out by increases in scientific knowledge. This raises two further questions.

1. 'Does *God* know the outcome of these situations that are

unpredictable to us?' God's omniscience must be such as to
know and to be able to track the minutiae of the fluctuations
whose amplification leads at the macroscopic level to one outcome rather than another. The 'incommensurability', as it is
called, of the real numbers we use to specify initial conditions
(that is, any variable quantity can never in practice be measured
to a sufficient number of decimal points to specify it completely)
means we need an unattainable, infinite series of decimal points
to give unlimited predictability even in a deterministic system.
This entails that there will always be a 'horizon of predictability'
for us – but not for an omniscient God who could always know
the initial conditions, even within a fluctuation, to any degree of
accuracy required to predict for a given interval ahead. (If these
conditions were subject to quantum 'fuzziness', then God's
knowledge would still be the maximum *possible*, in this case
probabilistic.)

2. 'Does God act within these situations to effect his will?
God would then be conceived of as acting, as it were, 'within'
these, for us, unpredictable situations in a way that, in principle,
could never be detectable by us and would always be consistent
with our scientific knowledge of the situation. To do this, God
would be conceived of as actually manipulating quanta, atoms
and molecules in these initiating fluctuations in the natural
world in order to produce the results that God wills. But
such divine action would be just as much 'intervention' as it
would have been when postulated in relation to the outdated
mechanistic world view – the finger of God, as it were, actually
pushing molecules, or quanta around.

It is concluded that this newly-won awareness of the unpre-
dictability-for-us that is inherent in many natural processes and
systems does not, of itself, help directly to illuminate what
Austin Farrer called the 'causal joint' of how God acts in the
world – where the actual interface is at which God influences
events in the world. Talk of the 'causal joint' between God and
the world is, in fact, not very appropriate for a world in which

influences operate through many, multiply-interlocked levels in the complex systems that constitute it. It is on this major feature of the world as perceived by the sciences that attention must now be focussed.

Whole-part constraints (or downward, or top-down, causation) As already described, in a number of natural situations real features of the total system-as-a-whole can be properly regarded as constraints upon events happening within the sub-systems at lower levels – events, which, it must be stressed, are in them-selves describable in terms of the sciences pertinent to that lower level. In the light of this, the world-as-a-whole can be seen to be a total system so that its general state can be a constraint upon what goes on at the myriad levels that comprise it. These new perceptions of the way in which constraints actually operate in our interlocking complex world provide a new resource for modelling how God could interact with it.

The total world system, it has been stressed, is to be seen as 'in God' who (uniquely) is present to it *as a whole*, as well as to its individual component entities – God is present to all spaces and all times if God interacts with the 'world' at this super-venient level of totality, then God's intentions could be imple-mented by making events happen in a 'whole-part' manner without abrogating the laws and regularities (or modifying the unpredictabilities-for-us) that characterize the myriad sub-levels of existence that constitute that 'world' – the sub-levels open to our observation. God is the ultimate Boundary Condition of all-that-is.

In thus speaking of God's interaction with the world, it has not been possible to avoid speaking of God's 'intentions', of God having purposes, thereby using the language of personal agency. For these ideas of whole-part constraint by God cannot be expounded without relating them to the concept of God as, in some sense, an agent, least misleadingly described as personal.

Updating of the model of personal agency for God's interaction with the world Over recent decades the pressure from the relevant sciences has been inexorably towards viewing the processes that occur in the human brain and nervous system, on the one hand, and the content of consciousness, our personal, mental experience, on the other, as two facets or functions, or ways of describing, one total unitive process and activity. Combining a non-dualist account of the human person and of the mind-body relation with the idea of whole-part constraint (or top-down causation) illuminates the way in which states of the brain-as-a-whole: (*a*) could be causally effective at the level of neurones, and so of action; and (*b*) could actually also be mental states to which non-reducible mentalist, including first person, language could legitimately refer.

The notion of whole-part constraint from the integrated, unitive mind/brain state to human bodily action and the recognition of the unity of the human mind/brain/body event *together* provide a fruitful clue or model for illuminating how one might think of God's interaction with the world. According to this suggestion, the state of the totality of the world-as-a-whole (all-that-is) would be known only to the omniscience of God and would be the field of the exercise of God's omnipotence at God's own comprehensive, omnicompetent level of apprehension. Just as our, human, personal subjectivity (the sense of being an 'I') is a unitive, unifying, centred influence on the conscious, willed activity of our bodies, and this is what characterizes personal agency – so God is here conceived of as the unifying, unitive source and centred influence on all-that-is. This furthermore suggests that the succession of the states of the system of the world-as-a-whole is also a succession in the experience of God, who is present to it all; and that this is a model for, is analogous to, the way (it may be postulated) a succession of brain states constitutes the succession of our thoughts. In this model, God would be regarded as exerting *continuously* whole-part constraints on the world-as-a-whole in a way analogous to that whereby we in our thinking can exert effects on our bodies in a whole-part manner. It is at this holistic level, it is suggested, that God interacts with the world to influence events by what can best be described as an 'input of information' (where, again, 'information' is used in the technical sense to indicate what differentiates different patterns of events of the same total energy). This does *not* mean that the world may be thought of as 'God's body', for God's being is distinct from that of the created world. The basis for the analogy above is that all-that-is constitutes an interlocking, interdependent system – supremely and uniquely known only to God in all its ramifications. This is certainly not the same *kind* of system as that of a human body, but it is nevertheless a *system* of unimaginable complexity in its crosslinking influences through time and space.

This holistic mode of action and influence on the world is God's alone and distinctive of God. Thereby God can shape and direct events at lesser levels so that the divine purposes are not ultimately frustrated and are attained. Such interaction could occur, as we saw, without ever abrogating at any point any of the natural relationships and inbuilt flexibilities and freedoms operative within the world.

Only God in God's own transcendence is present to the totality of all-that-is as well as, in God's immanence, also to the individual entities that comprise created existence. Hence only God could be aware of the distinctiveness of any state of that totality and what states might or might not succeed it in time. This divine knowledge would always be hidden from and eternally opaque to us, existing as we do at levels at which the conceptual language will never be available for apprehending God's own 'inner' life. The best that can be done is to stretch the language of personal experience as the least misleading language available to us.

On this interpretation, we are free to describe any events at our own level of existence in the terms (including scientific ones) which are available to us; and at the same time to regard those same events, whether private and internal, or public and external to all, as capable of manifesting God's intentions, that is to say, God's 'providence'. For God could have brought it about that they are what they are and not something else by that over-all comprehensive constraint which God can exert (but does not *necessarily* do so) in a whole-part constraining manner upon any 'lower-level' event (or pattern or conjunction of events) occurring in the world. God is thus to be conceived of, not only as sustaining in existence the creative processes of the world, but also as all the time the *continuing* supra-personal, unifying, unitive Agent acting upon all-that-is, as Godself purposes. God thereby can influence particular events, as well as more general patterns and trends, as God chooses. Such an influence would never be observed by us as a divine 'intervention', as an inter-ference with the course of nature and as a setting aside of its natural, regular relationships.

In conclusion, it would seem that new perspectives afforded by the natural sciences on the processes of the world, including especially those on whole-part constraint, and on the unity of the human-brain-in-the human-body, provide not only a new con-text for the debate about how God might be conceived to inter-act with the world but also give new conceptual resources for modelling it.

This approach has stimulated a further insight into how the continuing interaction of God with the world-as-a-whole might best be envisaged – namely, as analogous to that of an input of information, rather than of energy. But since God is 'at least personal', such a flow of information is more appropriately described as a 'communication' by God to the world of God's purposes and intentions. This raises the question of whether or not there exists within the whole range of levels of complexity any created entity capable of discerning divine purposes and intentions encoded in the events of the world. Clearly human beings have thought they have done so, hence our concern in the following is with the possibility and nature of God's communi-cation with humanity.

2

God and Humanity

God's interaction with a world containing humanity

The previous chapter was concerned with God's interaction with the world as a whole and I adduced considerations that led us to regard God as 'at least personal'. The traditional model of personal agency was used for God's interaction with the world as whole – amplifying it with an emphasis on the role of whole-part constraint and on body-mind unity in any contemporary account of human action. The notion of a flow of 'information' (in the sense of alteration of patterns of events in the world) was also employed to describe the kind of whole-part constraint involved in the processes of human agency. Furthermore, recognition that God is 'at least personal', that is, in some sense 'supra-personal', also led to the recognition that God would be expected to be *self*-communicating.

In human experience the material objects that constitute part of what appears to us as 'outward' reality – those things which occupy space and time and are, in principle, perceptible by our bodily senses – are distinguished from our 'inward' mental lives, which do not satisfy those conditions. There is also a further useful working distinction (Quick 1927: ch. 1) between the ways in which the 'outward' is related to us: the 'outward' can be either an *instrument* which takes its character from what is done with it: or it can be a *symbol* which takes its character from what is known by it. Similarly, the world (all-that-is) may be viewed as the *instrument* whereby God is effecting some cosmic purpose by acting on, or doing something with it. Or the world may be

Legend to fig. 1

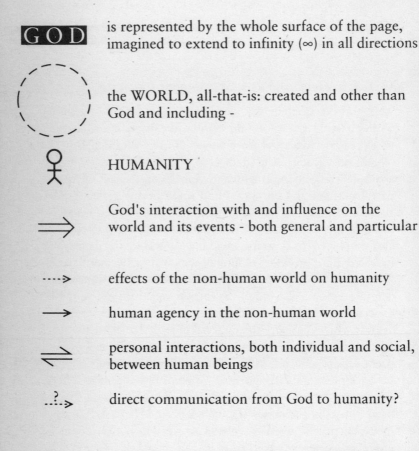

GOD is represented by the whole surface of the page, imagined to extend to infinity (∞) in all directions

the WORLD, all-that-is: created and other than God and including -

HUMANITY

God's interaction with and influence on the world and its events - both general and particular

effects of the non-human world on humanity

human agency in the non-human world

personal interactions, both individual and social, between human beings

direct communication from God to humanity?

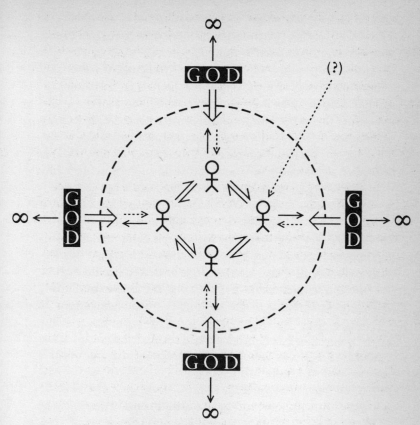

Figure 1. Diagram representing spatially the interaction between God and the world, including humanity.

viewed as the *symbol* in and through which God is signifying and expressing God's eternal nature to those who have eyes to see: that is, revealing Godself within it.

The account of how God interacts with the world was chiefly concerned with devising a model for the former 'instrumental' kind of relation. Now it is necessary to think through the implications of this model for explicating what Quick called God's 'symbolic', that is, God's communicating relation to the world. In doing so, both the context and the means of any possible revelation to humanity of God in the world and how it is actually experienced will have to be clarified. One feature of the world – its multi-layered levels of complexity – suggests that different 'levels' in the natural hierarchy of complexity would be expected to differ in the extent to which they can communicate to us God's meanings and purposes. Furthermore the transcendence-in-immanence that characterizes human persons could well be the basis for a special role for humanity in this communicating relation of God in and to the world. For human beings seem to be uniquely capable of a personal relation to God and so of being sensitive to any *self*-communication of the divine.

The earlier discussion of God's interaction with the world is summarized in Figure 1 on p. 25, in a necessarily inadequate but, it is hoped, a helpful way.

Figure 1 attempts to express on a two-dimensional surface the relation and interactions between different modes of being – it is an ontological representation (rather like a Venn diagram). The two kinds of relation of God to everything else ('the world', including humanity) are distinguished by God being denoted by the (imagined) infinite planar surface of the page (extended to infinity) on which the representations of everything else are printed. This may be regarded as a two-dimensional representation of the world being 'in God' and of God as being 'more than' the world, ontologically. God has a different *kind* of existence from everything else (which is why we attribute 'transcendence' to God). So the representations of the world and humanity and their inter-relations are located *on* the page and are distinct from the page itself, which is present 'under' and 'to' those shapes, as God is to all that God has created. For God is the circum-ambient and underlying and ultimate Reality from whom all else derives its dependent being. In Figure 1, humanity is placed inside the circle denoting the world to indicate that humanity is an evolved part of nature. No time scale has been represented and the limitations of this kind of representation must always be borne in mind!

It is clear that all mutual interactions between human beings and the world (the solid and dashed single-shafted, double-headed arrows of Fig. 1) are through the mediation of entities, structures and processes in the physical world of which human beings are part and in which human actions occur. Furthermore all interactions between human beings (the pairs of solid single-headed arrows in Fig. 1) occur through the mediation of the contents of the physical world (including the cultural heritage coded on to material substrates – tapes, books, pictures, etc.). Such interactions include, of course, *communication* between human beings, that is, between their states of consciousness. On the non-dualist account of the human person adopted here, states of consciousness are also, under one description, patterns of events within human brains. Hence all the interactions within the world (inside the dotted circle of Fig. 1) can be described as relationships and mutual interactions between the entities, structures and processes of the world. Since these mutual interactions include those in which communication occurs between human beings, this raises the question of how, within such a framework of understanding, one can conceive of God's communication with humanity, the self-communication of God to humanity. This in turn raises the traditional question of how God might reveal Godself to humanity – how, in what way, can we conceive of God communicating with and to humanity in the light of the foregoing?

Revelation and human experience

In communication between human beings some of our actions, gestures and responses are more characteristic and revelatory of our distinctive selves, of our intentions, purposes and meanings, than are others. 'It's not what you say but the way you're saying it.' This prompts us to seek in the world for those events and entities, or patterns of them, which unveil God's meaning(s) most overtly, effectively and distinctively – constituting what is usually called 'revelation'. However, as Rowan Williams (1986: 200) has warned: 'the model of revelation as a straightforward 'lifting of a veil' by divine agency has to be treated with caution . . . 'Revelation' is certainly more than a mythologically-slanted metaphor for the emergence of striking new ideas . . . the language of revelation is used to express the sense of an initiative that does not lie with us and to challenge the myth of the self-constitution of consciousness.' That is, in revelation God is pre-supposed to be *active*.

The ways now in which such a revealing activity of God might be thought to occur in the different ranges and contexts of human experience need to be examined. They will be graded according to the increasing extent to which God is experienced as taking the initiative in making Godself explicitly known.

General revelation If the world is created by God then it cannot but reflect God's creative intentions and thus, however ambiguously, God's character and purposes; and it must go on doing so if God continuously interacts with the world in the way we have proposed. The *locus classicus* of this concept of a 'general revelation' to all humanity is, of course, in St Paul's letter to the Romans (1.19, 20 NEB): 'For all that can be known of God lies plain before their [men's and women's] eyes; indeed God's own self has disclosed it to them. Ever since the world began his [God's] invisible attributes, that is to say his ever-lasting power and deity, have been visible to the eye of reason, in the things he has made.'

This expresses the belief that there is a knowledge of God, however diffuse, which is available to all humanity through reflection on the character of the created world, its entities, structures and processes, and in personal and social experience. That there should be such a knowledge of the divine nature and purposes which is mediated through the world, including humanity, is entirely coherent with the understanding of God's interaction with the world as represented in Figure 1. The double arrows denote an input into the world from God that is both influential in the whole-part constraining manner already discussed, and thereby an input of 'information' in the sense of altering patterns of events in the world. The states of human brains can properly be considered to be such patterns, so that it is intelligible in this framework how God might implant the means for knowledge of Godself within the world and consequently in human experience. Hence, in the model we are deploying, there can be a general revelation to humanity of God's character and purposes in and through human knowledge and experience of the world.

Revelation to members of a religious tradition Belonging to a religious tradition provides one with the language and symbols to articulate one's awareness of God at any instant and as a continuing experience. Immersion in a tradition through ritual, liturgy and its devotional activities provides an ever-renewed opportunity of making real in the present those significant past experiences of individuals and groups in that community which are regarded as especially revelatory of God. The tradition helps the individual both to enrich and to have the means of identifying his or her own experience of God. Thus there is a general experience of the ordinary members of a continuing religious community which may properly be regarded as a mode of revelation that is an enhancement of, and as more explicit than, that general revelation to humanity already discussed. As Grace Jantzen (1987: 122) has remarked, with respect to Christianity (though no doubt it would also be applicable to adherents of the other monotheistic faiths):

> A great many Christians would say that they continue in their faith in God because, in spite of all the problems . . . they would be fundamentally untrue to their own experience if they abandoned their faith . . . they are indicating the sense of the presence of God in their daily, ordinary lives, giving purpose to routine, providing courage, comfort, and hope, strengthening and deepening their moral commitment and sensitivity, leading them to worship and praise.

This kind of what one might call 'religiously general' revelation arises when there is a confluence between, on the one hand, the streams of general human experience and general revelation and, on the other hand, those of the recollected and re-lived particular and special revelations of God that a tradition keeps alive by its intellectual, aesthetic, liturgical, symbolic and devotional resources. These all nurture the unconscious experience of the adherent to that tradition and so shape their conscious awareness of God.

Special revelation   Some experiences of God by individuals, or groups of individuals, are so intense and subsequently so influential that they constitute initiating, 'dubbing' experiences which serve in the community to anchor later references to God and God's relation to humanity, even through changes in the metaphorical language used to depict that ultimately ineffable Reality. So it is not improper to seek in the world for those events and entities, or patterns of them, which reveal God's meaning(s) most overtly, effectively and distinctively. The Judaeo-Christian tradition has, more than most other religious traditions, placed a particular emphasis on God's revelation in the experienced events of a history – that of Israel and, for Christians, that of the life, teaching, death and resurrection-exaltation of Jesus of Nazareth, viewed as the consummation of the preceding revelation to Israel. This is what is usually called 'special' revelation and certainly involves that 'sense of an initiative that does not lie with us' referred to by Williams, indeed a sense of its being initiated by *God*. Such special revelation has been regarded by Christians as recorded particularly in the Bible – but how we are to receive this record today in the light of critical and historical study is a major issue in contemporary Christianity. This is not our immediate concern except to note that this issue is but a contemporary manifestation of the dialogue which originates in the need for all generations subsequent to the initiating, putatively revelatory, events to sift and winnow them in the light of their own experience and knowledge – and so transmit them to their successors. As indeed in the Bible itself, each generation in a religious tradition is involved in a dialogue with its own past and (as also in the Bible itself) often re-writes and recasts it, even sometimes consciously controverting it from a new perspective.

In involving itself with such a dialogue with its past, a community is also *ipso facto* engaged in a dialogue with God in its own times. David Brown (1985: 52-98) has developed a strong case for using this model of divine dialogue for special revelation as being one that preserves both the divine initiative and freedom as well as human freedom:

> . . . revelation is a process whereby God progressively unveils the truth about himself and his purposes to a community of believers, but always in such a manner that their freedom of response is respected . . . the notion of dialogue fully acknowledges that God's communication with man takes place in very specific contexts with certain things already assumed at each stage, an already existing canon of assumptions . . . that . . . inevitably shapes both the present experient's response to a particular experience and also what it is possible for God to put into that particular experience by way of content. (Brown 1985: 70)

To postulate such a model of dialogue rests on an interactionist understanding of God's relation to the world, along the lines we have been developing. Moreover this dialogue, as Brown (1990) has also cogently argued, is not confined only to the exchange of words and ideas but, even more profoundly, consists in the creative transformation of natural symbols in our unconscious.

Revelation and 'religious experience' This attempt to discriminate between modes of revelation according to the degree to which God is experienced as taking the initiative in making Godself explicitly known is helpful up to a point. But there must be avoided the not uncommon tendency to press the distinctions too sharply and to ignore the smooth gradations between the different categories of revelation already distinguished. For example, it has been shown (David Hay 1990) that between a third and a half of the population of certain 'Western' countries (the USA, Great Britain, and Australia) respond positively to questions such as 'Have you ever been aware of or influenced by a presence or power, whether you call it God or not, which is different from your everyday self?' or 'Have you ever felt as though you were very close to a powerful spiritual force that seemed to lift you out of yourself?' According to one survey in Great Britain carried out in 1986 'if one includes responses claiming some sort of premonition as a religious experience, the total rises to two-thirds of the population' (David Hay 1990: 57), which far exceeds active membership of religious institutions. As might be expected, the proportion reporting (David Hay 1990: Table 5, p. 83) religious experience is greater amongst those claiming an institutional, religious adherence, but the significant point for our present purposes is how widespread such experience is, even in the secularized West, and that it is continuous in its distribution over those who are members of a religious community and those who are not. The evidence is that the boundary between 'general' revelation and revelation to members of a religious tradition is very blurred. But so also is that between the latter and 'special' revelation. For there are well-documented accounts over the centuries of devotional and mystical experiences among those who do belong to a religious tradition. These are regarded by them as experiences, and so revelations, of God. Such experiences of God partake of the character of many of those that are usually included within the category of 'special' revelation. Indeed the believers having these experiences recognize their adherence to the tradition which enshrines the 'special' revelations and through whose resources of language, symbol and imagery these experiences are expressed.

It is also widely recognized that the classical distinction between 'natural' and 'revealed' theology has proved difficult to maintain in modern times. For it can be held that the only significant difference between supposedly 'natural' and supposedly 'revealed' insights is that the former are derived from considering a broader (though still selected) range of situations than the latter. The same could also be said of the sub-sequently more widely favoured distinction between 'general' and 'special' revelation, for the range of, and overlap between, the means whereby insights are gained into the divine reality has had to be recognized. For in the end, as David Pailin (1983: 506) puts it, the ultimate justification is 'by showing that the resulting understanding is a coherent, comprehensive, fruitful and convincing view of the fundamental character of reality'.

There is, in fact, a very real danger of bracketing off 'religious' experiences from the rich variety of human experience – in all its complex physical, aesthetic, intellectual, personal and social forms. Remember the remark of William Temple (1931: 25): 'By religious experience we ought to mean an experience which is religious through and through – an experiencing of all things in the light of the knowledge of God.' It is true that for the religious believer the whole of life can be revelatory of God. Nevertheless, 'special' revelations can occur and be identified. When they do so, it is usually among members of a religious

tradition (itself preserving earlier special revelations) who themselves experience God in their own way and, as human beings,
also in the way common to the rest of humanity.

There is then a genuine gradation but there are also real
differences in intensity and the degree of explicitness with
which these experiences are received as revelations of *God* as its
initiator – rather as a variegated and rough terrain may be
accentuated to give rise to distinctive hills and even sharp peaks
without loss of continuity. It is useful to have a word to denote
the more prominent of these knolls and eminences among the
human experiences of God that will include all experiences in
the whole range which have become sufficiently articulated to
the one experiencing to be significant both for them and for
others if adequately communicated to them. The only available
adjective appears to be the word 'religious', in spite of its unfor-
tunate connotations for many (e.g., its association with less than
attractive 'religious institutions' and with the baneful history of
'religion' at many times and places – as well as its frequent con-
fusion with 'religiosity'). But there is a more positive reason for
continuing to use the term 'religious experience'. For religious
experience, in the sense elaborated here, has played an important role in recent years in inductive, cumulative arguments
which claim to warrant belief in God – or, rather, to render the
existence of God more probable than not and so being, to that
extent, rational arguments.

This significance assigned to religious experience in philosophical theology renders even more urgent the need to address
questions that are implicit in the foregoing considerations,
namely: 'How does our understanding of God's interaction
with the world including humanity relate to revelatory human
experiences of God?', 'How can the notion of religious
experiences be accommodated by, be rendered intelligible in, be
coherent with, the understanding of God's interaction with the
world that we have developed in the light of the perspectives of
science?' That is:

How can we think of God communicating with humanity?

To attempt to answer this question different kinds of religious experience will first be distinguished. The way in which human persons communicate with each other will then be examined to see if it can give us any clues about how God might communicate with humanity. The relation between religious experience and the way in which we have been conceiving that God interacts with the world, including humanity – that is the question of *how* God might be thought of as communicating with humanity – can then be investigated.

Varieties of religious experience   Figure 2 (on p. 36) reproduces in outline the classifications of religious experience given by Richard Swinburne (1979: ch. 13) and by David Brown (1985: 33-51). Swinburne (1979: 246) defines a 'religious experience' as (his words) 'an experience which seems (epistemically) to the subject to be an experience of God (either of his just being there, or doing or bringing about something) or of some other supernatural thing [sic!]'. The distinction in Figure 2 between religious experiences that are 'mediated' and 'unmediated' by something sensory is based on whether or not, respectively, there is an answer by the subject to the question, 'What was it about your experience which made it seem to you that you were having an experience of God?'. If there is an answer to this question, then the experience is 'mediated'; if none, 'unmediated'. Figure 2 classifies the phenomenology of religious experience and is concerned with the *means* whereby God is known. It is with such modalities, rather than with the actual content of the experience of God, that we are concerned at this stage.

Communication between persons   We have been maintaining that personal language, with all its recognized limitations in this context, is the least misleading language to use of God, so it is appropriate to ask first: How do human beings communicate with each other and get to know each other, not only by descrip-

Figure 2   VARIETIES of RELIGIOUS EXPERIENCE

MEDIATED by something sensory				UNMEDIATED by something sensory
PUBLIC		PRIVATE		
Swinburne (1) Common, well-known phenomena Perceiving ordinary non-religious objects	(2) Perceiving very unusual public objects (may or may not involve violation of a natural law)	(3) Sensations describable by the normal vocabulary used for sensations of the five senses	(4) Sensations not describable by the normal vocabulary used for sensations of the five senses (these 'religious' sensations only analogous to the latter)	(5) No sensations Subject aware of God, or of a timeless reality . . . – 'just so seems to' the subject, but not through having sensations
Brown I Thematic experiences – where the theme or interpretative framework is believed to have been set by the divine. No unusual features.	II Sensory experiences. Unusual sensory perceptions, irrespective of whether or not the object so perceived is conceived of as existing in the external world (e.g. vision, dreams, auditions, etc.).		III Mystical experiences, of intimacy with the divine	IV Numinous experiences in which awe of the divine is the central feature

tion, but also by acquaintance – that is get to know what is, as we say, 'in each other's minds'?

All communication at its most basic level is mediated through the senses – hearing, sight, touch, taste, smell. The physical intermediaries are thus: vibrations in pressure in the air, electromagnetic waves, physical pressure, molecules, all constituents of the physical world. Our genes, culture, nurture and education have all enabled human beings to decode patterns of these physical intermediaries that convey information about the content of the consciousness of the one attempting to communicate. These patterns can be immensely complex, associated with long histories, and can weave subtle patterns in time, as with music and language, as well as in 'body language' and 'eye-to-eye' contact. In all these ways individual persons communicate with each other and also with the human community, both past and present.

The receptor of this 'information' in the individual person is the individual human brain which stores this variegated 'information' that constitutes knowledge of the inner state of other brains at different levels and integrates it into a perception of the other person in his/her totality. Such knowledge of the other person can be recalled, with varying degrees of rapidity and accuracy, into consciousness. On the non-dualist view espoused here, this process can be regarded as a re-activation of the brain to reproduce the original patterns that previously constituted this conscious awareness of the other person – as long as it continues to be recognized that these conscious 'mental' events are a non-reducible reality that is distinctive of the human-brain-in-the-human-body.

It seems that all the processes involved in inter-communication between human persons can be investigated and described at different levels by the methods and concepts appropriate to the level in question without invoking any special 'psychic' medium, unknown to the natural sciences, as the means of communication. This is not to say that the meaning of what is communicated can be reduced simply to physical patterns in the media in question, for the interpretation of these necessitates a recognition of their distinctive kind of reality. Neither a musical sequence or a line of a poem is *merely* a succession of sounds – each has a distinctive meaning in its own context. However, it is to stress that all communication between human beings, even at the most intimate and personal level, is mediated by the entities, structures and processes of the world. The subtly integrated patterns of these means of communication do in fact allow mutual comprehension between two human individuals of each other's distinctive personhood. This knowledge of two persons of each other, this knowledge by acquaintance, is notoriously not fully expressible in any of the frameworks of interpretation appropriate to the various modalities of the interaction process.

Recognition of the rootedness of the means of inter-personal communication in the constituents of the world indeed does *not* diminish or derogate from the special kind of reality that constitutes persons and their mutual interactions. For in such communication between persons there occurs a subtle and complex integration of the received sense-data with previous memories of that person. This occurs under the shaping influence of a long-learnt cultural framework of interpretation that provides the language and imagery with which to articulate the relation in consciousness. So recognition of the physical nature of the means of communication between persons in no way diminishes the uniqueness and 'in depth' character that can pertain to personal relationships at their most profound level for the individuals concerned. These are, indeed, often the most 'real' and significant experiences of people's lives. There remains an inalienable uniqueness and, indeed, mystery concerning the nature of the individual person and of the nature of the interaction between two persons. Not only the sense of personhood, of being a human person, but also awareness of inter-personal relations are unique, irreducible emergents in evolved *homo sapiens*.

Relation of religious experience to God's interaction with the world If God interacts with the world in the way already proposed, through a kind of whole-part constraining influence on the whole world system, how do we think God could communicate with humanity in the various kinds of religious experience (Figure 2)? It has been noted that the inter-personal relationships which we know of occur through the mediation of the constituents of the world. This suggests that all religious experience that is mediated through sensory experience (left of the double line in Figure 2) is intelligible in the same terms as that of the inter-personal experience of human beings. It is therefore plausible to think of God as communicating with human persons through the constituents of the world, through all that lies inside the dashed circle representing the world in Figure 1. God is seen as communicating through such mediated religious experiences by imparting meaning and significance to constituents of the world or, rather, to patterns of events among them. This may properly be thought of as a 'flow of information' from God to humanity, so long as the reductive associations of such terms are not deemed to exclude, as they need and should not, inter-personal communication. Thereby insights into God's character and purposes for individuals and communities can be generated in a range of contexts from the most general to the special. So conceived, God's means of self-revelation in human experience would then partake of the same character as that in the patterns of constituents and events in the world – those elaborated in the interpretations of the natural and human sciences and history evoked by the organized study of nature and humanity. However, the concepts, language and means of investigating and appraising these experienced 'signals' from God would operate at their own level and not be reducible to those of the natural and human sciences. The interpretation of mediated religious experience would have its own autonomy in human inquiry – theology cannot be reduced without remainder to sociology or psychology, or *a fortiori* to the biological and physical sciences.

What about the 'unmediated', private forms of religious experience (on the right of the double line in Figure 2)? Brown (1985: 37, 42-51) sub-divides them into: the *mystical* 'where the primary import of the experience is a feeling of intimacy with the divine' and the *numinous*, 'those experiences where awe of the divine is the central feature'. Swinburne (1979: 251) divides them, on the one hand, into: 'the case where the subject has a religious experience in having certain sensations . . . not of a kind describable by normal vocabulary'; and, on the other hand, religious experiences in which 'the subject . . . is aware of God or of a timeless reality . . . it just so seems to him, but not through his having sensations'.

These finer discriminations matter less in our present context than the fact that these analyses of Brown and Swinburne explicate such 'unmediated' experiences of God. In such instances, is it necessary to postulate some action of God whereby there is a direct communication from God to the human consciousness that is not mediated by any known natural means, that is, by any known constituents of the world – for example, David Jenkins' notorious 'divine laser-beam' (1987: 4)? Is there, as it were, a distinctive layer or level within the totality of human person-hood that has a unique way of coming into direct contact with God? This was certainly the assumption when the human person was divided into ontologically distinct parts, one of which (often called the 'spirit' or the 'soul') had this particular capacity. If we assume *that*, there would have to be added to Figure 1 the (dotted) arrows going *directly* from God to wherever we located this entity ('spirit' or 'soul') in the human person – and not mediated at all through anything else in the world.

Now we cannot but allow the possibility that God, being the *Creator* of the world, might be free to set aside any limitations by which God has allowed his interaction with that created order to be restricted. However, we also have to recognize that those very self-limitations which God is conceived of as having self-imposed are postulated precisely because they render coherent the whole notion of God as Creator with purposes that are being implemented in the natural and human world we actually have, and which the sciences increasingly unveil. Such considerations also make one very reluctant to postulate God as communicating to humanity through what would have to be seen as arbitrary means totally different in kind from any other communications to human consciousness. These latter include the most intensely personal inter-communication but even this, as we saw above, is comprehensible as mediated subtly and entirely through the biological senses and the constituents of the world.

The psychosomatic unity of the human person, both on scientific and biblical grounds is here being assumed on both scientific and biblical grounds. Hence, to be consistent, even this particular kind of apparently 'unmediated' capacity for experiencing God cannot but be regarded as a mode of functioning of the total integrated unity of whole persons – persons who communicate with other persons in the world through the world's own constituents. This communicating nexus of natural events includes, for human beings, not only human 'sense data' and the human use of knowledge in the objective sense, but also all states of consciousness. So *within* the world, there has to be included all the states of the human brain that are, under another description, the contents of the unconscious as well as of consciousness. This will include all that the individual has stored in his or her lifetime in the form of symbols and possibly those archetypes which Jung has postulated as operating at these deep levels of the person. This process of storage and accumulating both conscious and unconscious resources is mediated by all the varied ways in which communication to humanity can occur – and all these ways of communication have been seen to be effected through the natural constituents of the world and the patterns of events which occur in them.

Hence when human beings have an experience of God apparently '*un*mediated' by something obviously sensory, they can do so by a communication from God through their recollected memories, the workings of the unconscious and everything that has gone into their *Bildung*, everything that has made them the persons they are. All of which is mediated through patterns in the constituents of the world, including brain patterns. This is entirely consistent with such experiences of God being the fruit of much self-discipline and quietly allowing God so to communicate. 'Be still and know that I am God', the psalmist advised (Ps. 46.10). Experiences of God are indeed often ineffable, incapable of description in terms of any other known experiences or by means of any accessible metaphors or analogies. This characteristic they share with others, such as aesthetic and inter-personal experience which are unquestionably mediated through patterns in the events of this world. In relationships with other persons, we only get to know them if they choose to reveal to us their 'innermost selves', as we say. In such a mutual relation an initiative is taken so that the revealing of one to the other can occur, again through natural means. There is no reason why God's communicating to us through the undoubtedly subtle means we have been trying to discern should not also be the result of an initiative from God – in other words, a 'revelation'. Such revelations could take the variety of forms that we have already described and would all be mediated by the constituents of the world and through patterns of natural events, yet could nonetheless be definitive and normative as revelations. Moreover, even those revelations from God which are experienced purely 'mentally', as it were, and as apparently 'unmediated', fall within this description. For if, as we have argued, God can influence patterns of events in the world to be other than they otherwise would have been but for the divine initiative – and still be consistent with scientific descriptions at the appropriate level – then it must be possible for God to influence those patterns of events in human brains which constitute human thoughts, including thoughts *of* God and a sense of personal interaction *with* God.

On examination, therefore, it transpires that the distinction between 'mediated' and 'unmediated' religious experiences breaks down because the 'unmediated' in fact involve the constituents of the world, and patterns of events in them, just as much as the 'mediated' ones. This distinction refers not so much to the means of communication by God as to the nature of the content of the experience – just as the sense of harmony and communion with a person far transcends any description that can be given of it in terms of sense data, even though they are the media of communication. We simply *know* we are at one with the other person; in contemplation similarly the mystic can simply be 'aware of God . . . it just seems so to him' (as Swinburne puts it); and both experiences can be entirely mediated through the constituents of the world. The involvement of the constituents of the world in the so-called 'unmediated' experiences of God is less overt and obvious because in them God is communicating through subtle and less obvious patterns in the constituents of the world and the events in which they participate. These latter include the patterns of memory storage and activity of the human brain, especially all those operative in communication at all levels between human persons (including *inter alia* sounds, symbols and possibly Jungian archetypes), and the artefacts that facilitate this communication. Such address from God can come unexpectedly and uncontrived by the use of any apparently external means: thus it seems to the one having the experience as *un*mediated, even though it depends on a long history of mediation through the constituents of the world.

This account of the way in which God communicates to humanity through the constituents of the world and through the patterns of events in which they are involved assumes that God is able to shape these events and these patterns to convey his meanings, his intentions and purposes, to humanity. This implies that some events and patterns of events in the constituents of the world are what they are and not something else because God has willed them so to be in order to communicate with humanity. In other words, this understanding of how God communicates with humanity rests on an interpretation of God's interaction with the world, such as the one given in the first chapter, in terms of a whole-part, holistic influence expressing God's intentions and purposes, which renders particular actions of God in the world feasible and consistent with scientific accounts of natural events. What the treatment in this chapter has been indicating is that it is also intelligible how God can communicate *personally* to human beings within a world coherently and consistently with the descriptions of that world given at other levels by the natural and human sciences.

All the above can be held to describe how God, according to all the evidence, communicates with humanity consistently with the way God has made the world. But does God allow Godself occasionally to set aside, as it were, God's divinely self-limited relation to creation to communicate with humanity in some unique way for a special purpose? Whether or not God has done so is a question of the evidence, which we recognize would have to be exceptionally strong historically to be convincing.[1]

The way in which God communicates with humanity that has been elaborated in the foregoing depends, as does the previously

---

[1] Some readers may be surprised that at no point have I invoked the supposed evidence for non-physical communication between human beings (e.g., extra-sensory perception) and even between human beings and matter (e.g., psychokinesis, etc.). The evidence for these is still highly disputed, not least amongst the scientific community, so that they cannot form the basis of any generally accepted reliable model for understanding inter-human communication, let alone that of God with humanity (for a survey see Broughton 1992). If they ever were proven to general assent, they would then fall into the category of natural features of the world and the arguments in the text would then also apply to them – they could then be one of the modes whereby God communicates with humanity. But while their status is still widely held to be *sub judice*, and indeed inconsistent with what we know about the world through the sciences, they cannot form the basis of any of our theological models. The validity of religious experience, that is, the authenticity of God's communicating with humanity does not depend on, and certainly has no vested interest in, the reality of such phenomena and even less in that of the so-called occult.

developed model of God's interaction with the world, on a strong doctrine of God's immanence in the world – of God's presence in, with, under and through the many levels of the fabric woven by the processes of the natural and human world in the fabric of its entities, structures and processes – and most distinctively and fully at the level of the personal. At the level of the human, and so of the personal, there might be anticipated an outreach of God's own ultimate Being into the becoming of the world; and of God thereby communicating God's own self – in the classical Christian terminology, God as 'Holy Spirit' coming to humankind and the presence of God being experienced. 'God as Holy Spirit' has been held to dwell in us, if we will allow that refining fire within. And the One who can so indwell can at the same time be encountered as the ultimately Other who transcends all and is immanent in all – and yet remains ineffable. On the inner throne of the interior castle of our personhood it might be possible for there to sit the One whose true being and becoming are beyond all talk of 'transcendence' and 'immanence'. That is the hint, hope and possibility opened up by the recognition that God both can and wills to communicate with us.

3

Human Being

This quest for a Christian theology which is consonant with the best-established perspectives on the natural world that the sciences can provide began (ch. 1) by reflecting on how God as Creator might be conceived of as interacting with and influencing that world. The question of how God could be best conceived of as communicating with humanity was then addressed (ch. 2). In the final chapter, the concern will be with what God has communicated to humanity, and in particular with that 'special revelation' which is in Jesus the Christ, claimed by Christians to be the very 'Word of God' to humanity. The existence and significance of this claimed self-communication of God to humanity can be judged only if we first undertake a further appraisal of what distinctively constitutes human nature, human being in the light of the sciences.

A significant element in these scientific perspectives is that human beings are inherently a part of nature, evolved out of the very stuff of the world. Not surprisingly, in view of the perennial interest of humanity to itself, many of the sciences have been concerned with human beings as such. Scientific perceptions of what we are continually change in content and focus of interest and this inevitably changes our understanding of the three-cornered relation of nature-humanity-God.

At this point we are chiefly concerned with what the sciences can tell us about human *being*, about what human beings *are*, the distinctive nature of humanity, and not with what human beings should be *becoming*, for such expositions have a distinctively prescriptive tone. Since the sciences, as such, aim rather to be descriptive in depicting natural realities, the whole theme of human 'becoming' will not be the principal subject of this chapter. The first and primary concern here is with the possible effects of the sciences on our understanding of human nature and any implications these might have for theology.

Levels: foci of interest and ranges of complexity

The distinctive, holistic qualities of human persons depend on the operation of processes occurring at many levels of complexity, each one of which is the focus of interest of a particular scientific discipline. Abrahamsen (1987: 355–388; Bechtel and Abrahamsen 1991: 256–259) has differentiated scientific disciplines by virtue of this variation in focus as they deal with the different levels within the human phenomenon. This gives rise to an epistemological scheme, illustrated in Figure 3 (pp. 48–49), which is concerned with levels of interest, and so of analysis. It is not intended as a grading according to any value judgments.

The following four focal 'levels' can be distinguished:

1. *the physical world*, whose domain can be construed, from a purely reductionist perspective, as that of all phenomena since everything is constituted of matter-energy in space-time, the focus of the physical sciences;
2. *living organisms*, the focus of the biological sciences;
3. *the behaviour of living organisms*, the focus of the behavioural sciences;
4. *human culture*.

Within some of these four levels of interest at least portions of hierarchies of complexity that consist of parts integrated into larger wholes can be found (in Figure 3, the horizontal, solid arrows represent such sequences). Moreover, within any particular analytical level of this scheme of disciplines, there are

Legend to Fig. 3

A 'hierarchy of disciplines' (an elaboration of Figure 8.1 of Bechtel and Abrahamsen).[17] 'Levels' correspond to foci of interest (see text). Level 4 is meant to give only an indication of the content of human culture (cf. Popper's 'World 3').

Solid horizontal arrows represent part-to-whole hierarchies of structural and/or functional organization. (N.B. Molecules and macro-molecules in level 1 are 'parts' of the 'wholes' in level 2). Dashed boxes represent sub-disciplines in particular levels that can be coordinated with studies at the next higher level (the connections are indicated by vertical, dashed, double-headed arrows). In each of the levels 1–3, examples are given of the *systems* studied which can be classified as being within these levels and also of their corresponding scientific disciplines. Level 2 elaborates additionally the part-whole hierarchy of levels of organization in the nervous system (after Fig. 1 of Churchland and Sejnowski).[18]

In level 2, the science of genetics has relevance to the whole range of the part-whole hierarchy of living systems and so, if included, would have to be written so as to extend across its entire width. CNS = central nervous system including the brain.

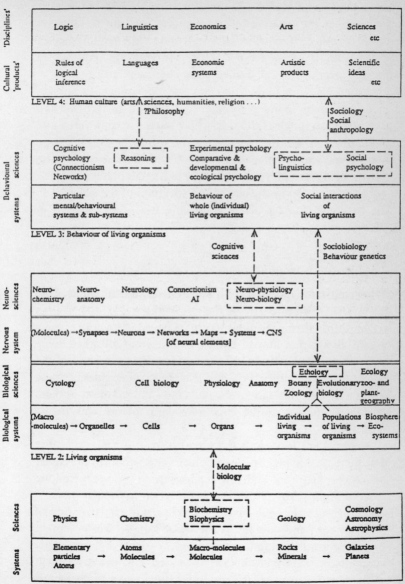

often sub-disciplines that form a bridge with an adjacent level by focussing on the same events or domains as does the next higher-level discipline. This allows for and shows the significance of interdisciplinary interactions. These 'bridges' are indicated in Figure 3 by the vertical, dashed arrows between levels.

Structures, functions and processes pertinent to human beings are to be found at focal levels 1 to 3 of this scheme and they also span much of the part-whole sequences in levels 1 and 2. No other part of the observed universe appears to include so many levels and to range over so much within these levels as do human beings (and level 4 refers only to human beings).

Let us now survey the current perspectives of the sciences on the nature of human being by making use of the schema of Figure 3.

The physical basis of human being (Focal level 1)

From time immemorial human beings have known that they are made up of the same stuff as the rest of the world – 'dust thou art, and unto dust shalt thou return' (Genesis 3.19 AV). Today we would say that human bodies, like those of all other living organisms, are constituted of the same atoms as the rest of the inorganic and organic world and that, to varying extents, these atoms also exist throughout the universe – indeed many of them originated in supernovae explosions long before this planet formed.

A significant feature of the physical level of natural reality pertinent to all living organisms is its capacity to form molecular structures that can undergo replication in self-perpetuating processes and patterns. This is the focus of 'molecular biology' which grew explosively from the discovery of the structure of DNA in 1953 and now forms the *bridge between levels* 1 and 2. This scientific discipline has entirely exorcised any ghostly remnants of the 'vitalism' that was mooted in the earlier half of the twentieth century to account for the distinctive characteristics of living organisms and so of 'living matter'. For molecular biology has made it increasingly implausible to think, as did the vitalist, of the qualities that emerge in evolution, not least in *homo sapiens*, as due to the *addition* of some entity to the very stuff of which living organisms and human beings are constituted. Rather, note is now taken of the emergence of new functions and capabilites consequent upon that growth in complexity which characterizes the evolution of biological systems. To find what does emerge it is necessary to consider:

Human beings as living organisms (Focal level 2)

All the biological sciences depicted in this level in Figure 3 can, in one way or other, include within their scope some aspects of human beings. This is not surprising in view of the evolutionary origins of humanity, as manifested particularly in the fact that some 98% of human DNA is the same as that of the DNA of chimpanzees. The evolutionary process itself is characterized by propensities, along certain lines of development, towards increase in self-organization, complexity, information-processing and -storage, consciousness, sensitivity to pain, and even self-consciousness (a necessary prerequisite for social and development and the cultural transmission of knowledge down the generations). Successive forms are likely to manifest more and more of these characteristics because of their favouring the natural selection of organisms that possess them. However, the actual physical forms of the organisms in which these propensities are actualized and embodied is contingent on the history of the conjunction of disparate chains of events. There can (*pace* Stephen Gould 1989: 51, passim) be overall direction and implementation of purpose through the interplay of chance and law, without a deterministic plan fixing all the details of the structure(s) of what emerges possessing personal qualities. Hence the emergence of self-conscious persons capable of relating personally to God can still be regarded as an intention of God continuously creating through the processes of that to which he has given an existence of this kind and not some other. (It certainly must have been 'on the cards' since it actually happened – with us!)

Remarkable and significant as is the emergence of self-conscious persons by natural processes from the original 'hot big bang' from which the universe has expanded over the last ten to twenty thousand million years, this must not be allowed to obscure another fact about humanity, namely how relatively recent is its arrival in the universe. If one takes the age of the Earth as two days of forty-eight 'hours' (1 such 'hour' = 100 million years), *homo sapiens* appears only at the last stroke of midnight of the second day. Hence other living organisms existed for some two thousand million or more years (= over 20 'hours' on the above scale) before our relatively late arrival and evolved through natural selection of the best procreators. We must not underplay the significance, therefore, also of the rest of the universe and of all other living organisms to God as Creator – even though we are able to depict only in imagination the kind of delight that God may be conceived to have in the fecund multiplicity and variety of created forms.

There are some other features of this history that any contemporary theological account of human origins and the nature of human being must also take into account. Evolution can operate only through the death of individuals – new forms of matter arise only through the dissolution of the old; new life only through death of the old. We as individuals would not be here at all, as members of the species *homo sapiens* if our forerunners in the evolutionary process had not died. Biological death was present on the Earth long before human beings arrived on the scene and is the pre-requisite of our coming into existence through the processes of biological evolution whereby God, we have argued, creates new species, including *homo sapiens*. Hence, in spite of St Paul (Romans 6.23), *biological* death, as such, cannot be the consequence of human 'sin' – whatever we decide *that* is.

Furthermore the biological-historical evidence is that human nature has emerged only gradually by a continuous process from earlier 'hominids' and that there are no sudden breaks of any substantial kind in the sequences noted by palaeontologists and anthropologists. Moreover there is no past period for which there is reason to affirm that human beings possessed moral perfection existing in a paradisal situation from which there has been only a subsequent decline. There was no golden age, no perfect past; there were no individuals, 'Adam' or 'Eve', from whom all human beings have now descended and declined and who were perfect in their relationships and behaviour. Mention of human behaviour brings us within the scope of level 3 but, as a prelude to examining this, there is a need to consider:

Human beings in the perspectives of sciences bridging the biological and the behavioural sciences (Between focal levels 2 and 3)

Sciences which bridge levels 2 and 3 include, on the one hand, cognitive science (or, 'cognitive neuroscience') and, on the other hand, sociobiology (called by some 'behavioural ecology') together with behaviour genetics.

Cognitive science is concerned with relating the different levels of analysis of information-processing (roughly, 'cognition') to action. It thereby forms a bridge between the purely biological neurosciences and the sciences of behaviour, and it is especially concerned with trying to understand how the mind-brain works, particularly in human beings. The detailed ways in which the various levels of analysis are being applied concern us less here than the now widespread realization by cognitive scientists that, in order to understand the relation between the behavioural, at one pole, and the molecular, at the other, understanding of all the intermediate levels of analysis, organization and processing is necessary.

This pressure to integrate the study of different levels is, it seems, generated by the nature of the very problems which cognitive scientists address. Moreover, what applies to the operation of the nervous system also applies to the operation of the brain as a whole. Nor is this simply now a methodological recommendation for even an in-principle materialist such as Patricia Churchland, in an article with T. Sejnowski, significantly entitled 'Perspectives in Cognitive Neuroscience' can recognize that

> The ultimate goal of a unified account does not require that it be a single model that spans all the levels of organization. Instead the integration will probably consist of a chain of models linking adjacent levels. When one level is explained in terms of a lower level this does not mean that the higher level theory is useless or that the high-level phenomena no longer exist. (Churchland and Sejnowski 1988: 744)

It is important to realize that it is because of the nature of the complexity of all biological systems, in general, including nervous systems and especially the human-brain-in-the-human-body, that no one description at any one level can ever be adequate and that therefore no one level has priority. The emergent properties and functions at the more complex levels of analysis, organization and processing are emergent *realities*.

The question of whether or not the human brain operates as a digital computer ('Artificial Intelligence' or by 'parallel distributed processing' (PDP – 'Connectionism') can only be settled by the ordinary processes of scientific research. The recognition of the many-levelled foci of such research means that there is no necessary conflict with either the investigations of human mental activity by the behavioural sciences (level 3) or, even more so, with those arising from the study of human culture. It may turn out that the human brain is a non-linear dynamic system, and so deterministic at the micro-level but unpredictable (certainly by us – but also by God? a key question) in its succession of overall states at the macro-level. If so, might we have here the physical correlate of the experience of consciousness, and so the warrant for giving an account in predominantly mentalistic terms of successions of what we experience as mental states, including those of the operations of 'free will'? None of this is inconsistent with that Christian anthropology, stemming from that of the Bible, which regards human beings as psychosomatic unities displaying a many-faceted personhood uniting many properties, abilities and potential relationships – and rooted in materiality.

Sociobiology may be broadly defined as the systematic study of the biological, especially the genetic, basis of social behaviour and, in relation to human beings, aims at exploring the relations between biological constraints and cultural change. It thereby encroaches, in the ambitions of at least some sociobiologists, on to level 4.

Clearly this whole development is of theological concern. For, by thus encompassing in one theory human culture and the non-human biological world (especially in its genetic aspects), sociobiology must inevitably influence our thinking about what human beings are. The debate is not entirely a replay of the old nature-nurture dichotomy for the subtlety and complexity of the strategies of gene perpetuation have undergone much revision and the many-levelled character of humanity is becoming more and more apparent. The emphatically evolutionary outlook of sociobiology raises no new questions for Christian theology that have not been raised by the general idea of evolution, both cosmic and biological, in relation to the affirmation of God as Creator. However, because of the predominantly reductionist tone in the writings of many sociobiologists, there has been a tendency to interpret human behaviour functionally merely as a strategy for the survival of genes. The theological response to such suggestions must, in its general thrust, be that which is made to any purely deterministic and reductionistic accounts of human behaviour – namely that it ignores all those realities that have emerged in human persons, such as those of the content of our consciousness, our self-consciousness and our free will. But in making such a riposte, theologians should nevertheless recognize, far more explicitly than they have done in the past, that human nature is exceedingly complex and that its basic foundational level is biological and genetic, however much it is overlaid by nurture and culture.

It has indeed been the purpose of general *behaviour genetics* since 1960, when it first came to be recognized as a distinct discipline, to examine 'the inheritance of many different behaviours in organisms ranging from bacteria to man' (Hay 1985: 1). Behaviour genetics is predominantly concerned with explaining individual differences within species. As a discipline it represents a fusion of the interests of genetics and psychology and moves between the two poles of a genetics of behaviour and a genetically-aware psychology (D. A. Hay 1985: 4, quoting Vale 1973: 872). This new sub-discipline is currently being vigorously applied to human beings. The research proceeds and, like all scientific research, as it does so it both clarifies and at the same time generates new problems. Even in their present form such studies are producing evidence of the genetic underpinning of much in personal behaviour and traits previously considered as entirely environmental and cultural.

Sociobiology and behaviour genetics cannot but influence our general assessment of human nature and, in particular, the degree of responsibility assigned to societies and individuals for their actions. The genetic constraints upon our nature and behaviour are, from a theistic viewpoint, what God has purposed shall provide the matrix within which freedom shall operate. Furthermore, theologians should acknowledge that it is this kind of genetically-based creature which God has actually created as a human being through the evolutionary process.

However, that genetic heritage cannot in advance itself determine the *content* of thinking and reasoning – even if it is the prerequisite of the possession of these capacities.

For example, to unravel the evolutionary and genetic origins of moral awareness is not to preempt its ultimate maturation in the moral sensitivity of self-aware, free, reasoning persons whose emergence in the created order God can properly be posited as intending.

Hence, the vital question becomes: what do we human beings make of these possibilities? The biological endowment of human beings does not appear to be able to guarantee their contented adaptation to an environment which is, for them, inherently dynamic. For they have ever-changing and expanding horizons within which they live individually and socially, physically and culturally, morally, emotionally and intellectually. In particular, when one reflects on the balanced adaptation of other living organisms to their biological niche, the alienation of human beings from non-human nature and from each other appears as a kind of *biological* anomaly within the organic world. Thus it is not surprising to find Eaves and Gross (1990: 17) discussing behaviour genetics, pointing out what they call the 'possible gulf' between the ecosystem in which human evolution occurred and the global environment into which humanity is now projected'; and going on to suggest that, the basically unethical, human favouring of genetic kin is a sign, at best, of tribal self-interest and 'that humans bring into the world by virtue of their ancestry biological baggage which is ill adapted to the present world'.

As human beings widen their environmental horizons, so they experience this 'gulf' between their biological past environment out of which they have evolved and that in which they conceive themselves as existing or, often, that in which they wish they existed – such experiences as contemplation of death, a sense of finitude, suffering, the realization (and non-realization) of human potentialities, steering a path through life to death. The mere existence of this 'gulf' between human experience and yearnings raises a problem for any purely biological account of human development. Why has, how has, the process whereby there have so successfully evolved living organisms finely tuned to and adapted to their environments failed in the case of *homo sapiens* to ensure this fit between lived experience and the conditions of their lives? It appears that the human brain has capacities which were originally evolved in response to an earlier environmental challenge but the exercise of which now engenders a whole range of needs, desires, ambitions and aspirations which cannot all be harmoniously fulfilled.

This engenders the further question of whether or not human beings have properly identified what their true 'environment' really is – that 'environment' in which human flourishing is possible. The complexity and character of the human predicament clearly involves more subtle levels of human nature than are the focus of level 2 or of the 'bridge' sciences to the next level. So we turn to

The sciences concerned with human behaviour (Focal level 3)

Some of the principal behavioural sciences and the systems on which they focus are indicated in level 3 of Fig. 3. Level 3 includes various forms of psychology which is, in its usage since the eighteenth century, the study of the phenomena of mental life. At first, this naturally included the (largely introspective) study of such human activities as perceiving, remembering, thinking and reasoning, but in the twentieth century until the mid-sixties psychology was dominated by behaviourism and psychoanalysis. Although there was some continued interest in cognitive and other mental processes (e.g., the 'Gestalt' school and Piaget and his successors), they were not in the forefront, or in the public image, of psychology.

This has now changed and mental processes have begun to be taken much more seriously. There has been a 'cognitive', 'consciousness' or 'mentalist' shift of emphasis in psychology that moves its focus of interest towards the content and activities of ordinary consciousness (sometimes neutrally, and somewhat curiously, denoted as 'self-modification'). Consciousness is now much more frequently regarded as a theoretical term that refers to realities whose existence is inferred from observation. How it is to be a thinking and feeling human being have again come on to the agenda of many of the behavioural sciences (level 3). Sperry (1988: 608), the brain scientist, asserted that there is a new openness in the behavioural sciences, not only in a 'downward' direction via cognitive science to the neurosciences, but also 'upward' to all those studies and activities that regard human consciousness and its content as real and worthy of examination and interpretation. There thus appears to be occurring a re-habilitation from a scientific perspective of the reality of reference of humanistic studies – in which theology should be included, if only because of its concern with religious experience. It also gives scientific credibility to what had never been doubted in theology – the pre-eminence of the concept of the 'personal' in the hierarchy of our interpretations of the many-levelled structure of the world of which humanity is an evolved constituent.

In all of this, the many-levelled approach that was seen to be necessitated by the exigencies of research in the cognitive sciences has to be extended further when the relationships between brain activity, mental experience and individual and social behaviour are under scrutiny. As the experimental psychologist Jeeves (1991: 70) says,

> . . . we need a hierarchy of levels and their corresponding categories of explanation in order to do justice to the complexity and richness of what we find when we study man . . . we are trying to discover how the stories at different levels correlate.

All this has important implications for the relation of science and religion. For instead of a dichotomy between, on the one hand, a dualism of 'body' and 'mind' (a common misapprehension of the Christian view of humanity) and, on the other, a reductive materialism, a new integrated 'view of reality' could emerge which, so Sperry (1988: 609) hopes, 'accepts mental and spiritual qualities as causal realities, but at the same time denies they can exist separately in an unembodied state apart from the functioning brain'. Thus the situation looks more encouraging for a fruitful dialogue between religion and the sciences of human behaviour than it has been for many decades.

The very multiplicity of the theories of psychology reminds us that focal level 3 theories are 'underdetermined by the facts', a characteristic they, in fact, share with the theories of the sciences of levels 1 and 2, though it is often less obvious with them. We have to tolerate the variety of theories in psychology as an inevitable consequence of the nature of their 'subject-matter' (*mot juste* in this instance!). However, this variety renders difficult any attempt to discern their implications for and possible effects on a Christian theology of humanity. That theology can properly claim, like all the major religious traditions, to have its own distinctive insights into human nature. No one of the theories of psychology may claim to be so definitive and so established that theology must come to terms uniquely with it. All, especially Jungian psychology, which is so sensitive to religious experience, can throw light on human personality and need to be considered by theology.

Furthermore a number of reflective psychologists remind us of the sense of 'mystery' about the nature of human personhood. Thus the psychologist Peter Morea (1990: 170) entitles the concluding chapter to his study of the theories of psychology 'The Mystery' for, he says: '. . . in our attempt to grasp personality scientifically, we experience something strange. As we reach out and are confronted by boundaries, we are filled with wonder at human personality, and we seem to touch mystery.'

Moreover, there is nothing static about the human condition;

again Morea (1990: 171): 'We are not so much human beings as human becomings.' He, too, points out the biological paradox of our lack of 'fit' with our environment as we perceive it. Human beings are a problem to themselves and for themselves. This implies the apparent paradox of God creating a mis-fit, or so it seems, in a world in which other living creatures are finely and appositely adapted to their environments. We are beings who comprehend and understand through the sciences vast tracts of the obscurities of the universe in which we find ourselves – only to be confronted with the most intransigent and unfathomable mystery when we face ourselves. As Morea (1990: 174) has expressed it:

> Thrown into the world I become a puzzle to myself; scientific theory has failed to find a solution to [this puzzle of] St Augustine . . . Religion has traditionally taught that human beings are made in the image of God. This would explain why we have difficulty in understanding personality. It would explain why, in our attempt to understand personality, we often experience wonder and awe. If human beings are made in God's image it would explain why – at the boundaries of our scientific knowing of human personality – we sometimes sense beyond the mystery of human personality a much greater Mystery.

The social sciences (Between focal levels 3 and 4)

The sciences variously designated as 'social' form a bridge between the behavioural sciences and culture. The more the sciences are concerned with the mental life and behaviour of human beings, the more they impinge on the normal concerns of the Christian community. It is worth noting, however, that the social conditioning of religious beliefs which the social sciences disentangle and reveal does not, of itself, settle any questions as to the *truth* of these beliefs.

The evolutionary process introduces another dimension into this complex relation between religious belief and social setting, namely that of evolutionary epistemology – the realization that cognition of its environment by a living organism has to be sufficiently trustworthy in its content to allow it to be viable under the pressures of natural selection. Thus sociobiologists have identified an 'altruism' that is exerted by individual organisms on behalf of the survival of those other members of the species that share its genes. Some social anthropologists (such as Donald Campbell) seeking to understand what could have brought into existence the socially necessary wider loyalties between non-kin human beings have increasingly identified the emergence of 'religiously' warranted imperatives as the explanation. The cumulative wisdom of the religious traditions has, by setting up norms related to the existence of a 'transcendental reality' other than human authority, contributed crucially, in the view of such investigators, to the process of human social organization, which is wider and more complex than that of any other living organism. In other words, humanity could only survive and flourish if it took account of social and personal values that transcended the urges of the individual embodying 'selfish' genes.

But does not this imply that these social and personal values, enshrined in moral codes and imprinted in ethical attitudes, are part of the realities with which we humans have to deal and of which we have to take account or otherwise die out? This increasingly accepted role of the religions of humanity in socio-cultural evolution points to the existence of values as constituting a reality-system that human beings neglect to their actual peril. Holmes Rolston (1987: 234) concluded his survey of the social sciences thus:

Nothing learned in social science forbids asking whether there is something transcendent to the human world, something sacred exerting its pull over society, and out of which the human natural worlds may be derived. What if there are some challenges and conflicts that a society can solve only religiously? . . . The fact is not so much that religion calls for an explanation outside itself in society. It is rather society that calls for an explanation outside itself in those realities to which religion points. Society, not just religion, is the effect.

Human culture and its products (Focal level 4)

Such perceptions take this quest into the domain of human culture, that of level 4 (Fig. 3). The 'cultural products' of level 4 are embodiments of human creativity in the arts and sciences and in human relations (including, I would add, relations to God) which are best, and in most cases only, discernible and transmissible by their own distinctive means through meaningful patterns created in what is received initially through our senses. These patterns, which are the means of communication between human beings and, we suggested, between God and humanity, are generated through historical formation in continuous cultures which invest them with meaning for enabling such communication. They thereby have the unique power of inducting humanity into an encounter with the transcendence in the 'other', whether in the form of a work of the creative, imaginative arts, or of another human person or of God, the Beyond within our midst. George Steiner (1989: 4) in his penetrating *Real Presences* has called all such encounters a 'wager on transcendence':

> . . . the wager on the meaning of meaning, on the potential of insight and response when one human voice addresses another, when we come face to face with the text and work of art or music, which is to say when we encounter the *other* in its condition of freedom, is a wager on transcendence.

He does not hesitate to point to its theological import:

The wager . . . predicates the presence of a realness . . . within language and form. It supposes a passage . . . from meaning to meaningfulness. The conjecture is that 'God' *is*, not because our grammar is outworn; but that grammar lives and generates worlds because there is the wager on God.

We can expect all such encounters with 'cultural products', all such 'wagers on transcendence', to communicate only in their own way, in their own 'language', with immediacy at their own level – and not to be reducible to the languages of others.

Such a robust assertion of the conceptual and experienced autonomy of what is communicated in human culture is reinforced by the re-habilitation of the subjective, of inner experience, in cognitive science and in psychology – in fact, in the recovery of the personal, the recognition of the reality of personhood. We do really seem to be witnessing a major shift in our cultural and intellectual landscape which opens up the dialogue between the human spiritual enterprise (broadly, 'religion') and that of science in a way long barred by the dominance of a mechanistic, reductionist, naturalism, of a kind thought erroneously to have been warranted by science itself. The human is undoubtedly biological, but what is distinctively human transcends that out of which and in which it has emerged.

This pressure for a wider perspective on humanity is being generated from within the sciences themselves (if not by all scientists, as such) in attempting to cope with the many levels of Figure 3. Is it too much to hope that we see here the first glimmerings for some time of a genuine integration between the humanities, including theology, and the sciences; and a breakdown of that dichotomy between the 'two cultures' that was engendered by the absence of any epistemological map on which their respective endeavours could be meaningfully located? All of this strengthens the claims of a *Christian* humanism not only within the domain of humanism as such, but also within that of theology – for Christian theology is (or should be) concerned above all else with the consummation of the human and with human flourishing both in this life and *sub specie aeternitatis*.

A theology of human being in the light of the sciences

Some of the threads of general, especially theological, import that can be extracted from the subtly woven and ever elaborating fabric of the sciences concerned with humanity can now be extracted and drawn together.

Those perceptions stemming from the sciences which, with some adjustments, could be considered as congenial, broadly speaking, to received traditional Christian theology, are that human beings are:

- *part of nature* and so,
- *contingent*, notably with respect to their actual physical form exemplifying the propensities in evolution to complexity, information-processing, and so to consciousness and self-consciousness;
- *many-levelled*, indeed uniquely so, encompassing all the levels 1–4;
- *conscious and self-conscious person*s, where 'person' refers to the unique integration of levels 1–4 to be found in humanity (recall the 'cognitive'/'mentalistic' turn in the behavioural sciences, especially psychology);
- nevertheless ultimately *mysterious in being 'persons'*.

There are, however, also scientific perceptions that challenge received Christian theology, namely, that:

- much more of *human behaviour has a genetic* (and so *evolved*) *basis* than was previously thought, in particular much that was described as 'moral' or 'sinful'; *human beings are a relatively recent arrival* in the universe (so what is the theological significance of the existence of other organisms?);

♦ *biological death is* not the 'wages of sin', but *the means of creation* through evolution;

♦ *there never existed a period of human perfection* (moral or otherwise) from which there could have been a historical 'Fall'.

The paradox of human becoming

These perspectives raise more acutely than ever the paradox of a humanity that is a kind of misfit in its biological environment – 'evolution seems to have played a nasty trick, bringing into existence human beings vast in their desire and potential, but minute in their fulfilment and satisfaction', concluded the psychologist Morea (1990: 171). Profound and even more extensive insights have been and still are forthcoming from contemporary novelists, poets and dramatists, as well as from historians and social philosophers – indeed all who have reflected on the enormities and degradations that mar our twentieth-century history. They speak of 'angst', 'alienation', 'false self-consciousness', 'one-dimensional humanity', 'disintegration', and much else.

In doing so they but reflect the perennial insights of the Judaeo-Christian tradition into the significance of the Adam-and-Eve myth, of the Augustinian notion of 'Fall' and of 'original sin' which have so dominated Western Christian theology. The general thrust of and truth in modern theological interpretations is well represented by the biblical scholar, Alan Richardson (1957: 14):

The doctrine of Original Sin is not so much an *a priori* theory as an empirical description of human nature; we all of us tend at every moment to put ourselves in the place of God by setting ourselves in the centre of the universe . . . the 'Fall' is an ingredient of every moment of human life; man is at every moment 'falling', putting himself in the centre, rebelling against the will of God. Adam is Everyman.

Human beings possess a self-consciousness, which by enabling them to be 'subjects' over against 'objects' *ipso facto* renders them out of harmony with themselves, with each other and with God – and so capable of, and actually, thwarting the divine purposes. Self-consciousness, by its very character as *self-consciousness*, has made human beings aware of what they might become – and of their failure to fulfil their potentialities and to satisfy their highest aspirations and has made them aware of personal death and human finitude, as well as enhancing suffering.

The above modern descriptions of the human state, as 'alienated', etc., all reflect a sense of incompleteness, a felt lack of integration and a widespread judgment that the life of human individuals in twentieth-century society has failed to live up to the hopes engendered by scientific technology. These hopes have foundered on the rock of the obduracy of self-will operating in a humanity inadequate through its own inner paralysis of will to the challenge of its newly won knowledge and power over the world. Contributing crucially to this paralysis is the failure of humanity to discern what it should be becoming – that is, what it *ought* to be. Thus it is that the greater intelligibility of the existence and rationality of the universe which is afforded by the postulate of the existence of God as Creator, the more it is in danger of collapsing in view of the enigmatic and paradoxical nature of the humanity which has been evolved within it. To put it more bluntly, what does God think God is doing in evolving the human being, this 'glory, jest and riddle of the world' as Pope described us in his *Essay on Man* (Epistle ii, 1.28), with our enormous potentiality both for creative good and for degradation and evil, and so for self-destructive and danger to the rest of the created world?

Our accounts of biology, genetics and psychology incline one to ground at least some of this widely intuited individual and social malaise in the levels on which these sciences focus. This serves to warn that no superficial palliatives will be able to achieve the consummation of human potentialities – transformation is needed of the total human being at the many levels of human existence in the individual and in society.

Furthermore, in exercising their freedom, human beings are always 'beings-on-the-way' (Macquarrie 1987: 172–5). Thus it is that philosophical and theological anthropologies are concerned with 'the realization of human nature as an emerging reality' (Macquarrie 1982: 3). In the 'search for humanity', the sciences do not provide data or even theories that can tell us what humanity should be becoming, individually and corporately. So it is pertinent to ask, in what range of human inquiries might such guidance and wisdom be found?

It was reported earlier that it is being increasingly urged by at least some social anthropologists that the religions of humanity have played a determinative role in the socio-cultural evolution of values, the formulation of what *ought* to be rather than what *is* so. For the power of social and personal values generated by the religions of humanity in socio-cultural evolution stems from their being grounded, so they believe, on experience of a pressing 'reality' which both transcends and inter-penetrates human self-awareness.

Summarizing the evidence accumulated by the Religious Experience Research Centre at Oxford, its founder could claim that: '. . . a large number of people even today possess a deep awareness of a benevolent non-physical power which appears to be partly or wholly beyond, and far greater than, the individual self' (Hardy 1979: 1). These well-documented experiences of a 'transcendental reality', to use Hardy's term, cannot simply be experiences of 'nothing-at-all'. Can these cognitive experiences of myriads of people and in many ages alone out of all human experiences – those that by encountering physical, biological, social and personal realities are conducive to human survival and flourishing – have *no* contact with any reality essential for human survival and flourishing? This is not what the role of religion that is beginning to be discerned in socio-cultural evolution suggests. Nor would any of those having such experiences believe that. Nor can anyone who, not blessed with such experiences, has immersed him or herself in a religious tradition that nurtures the numinous and the mystical believe it either. These experiences and the cumulative wisdom of the religious traditions point together to a level of human cognition whereby human beings become aware of the existence of an all-encompassing Reality that transcends all, yet is immanent in all existence, their relation with which is essential for human survival and flourishing. This Reality, humankind calls 'God'.

In this light, the religious experience of humanity is to be seen as constituted of a trial-and-error and conjecture-and-refutation process of interaction with that Reality, of encounter with God. For if that Reality exists, if there is a God, there could be nothing more important for humankind than to come into the most comprehending and comprehensive relation with him/her/it. For the establishing of such a relation would surely then be the basic condition for it to flourish both individually and as a species. For does not the human condition raise the profound question of what humanity's *true* environment really is? Thus it was that St Augustine (*Confessions* Book1 [1]1), after years of travail and even despair, addressed his Maker: 'You have made us for yourself and our heart is restless till it rests in you.'

For humanity has to reckon with the nature of that Reality whose name is 'God'. This 'God' is no stone idol or merely impersonal force. Such a 'God', it has to be acknowledged, is in principle greater than all else of which we can conceive, and cannot therefore, as the source and meaning of all-that-is, be less that personal. God seeks to communicate to humanity both God's own meaning and God's own very self. There is therefore every reason to take with the utmost seriousness that long search by humanity for wisdom about their nature and true destiny which is represented in the religious traditions. Moreover, if God is a self-communicating God who penetrates all-that-is, then we have to reckon with the outreach of God *to* humanity and the meanings to and for humanity that God is conveying. After all, if God created us, God must be presumed to know what God wants to make of us. Indeed, since the signals concerning human fruition and consummation that come from scientific study of the natural, including the human, world are both ambiguous and indicative of dangerous possibilities, we would be wise to examine what *God* may have been communicating to humanity concerning its fruition, consummation and even perfectibility. It might even be that human personhood, nurtured by the natural order for this very purpose, can only come to be what the divine purpose has intended all along for it, if and when *God*, God's own self, comes to human beings to bring them to the fruition of a humanity taken up into the divine. To explore the possibility of, and any evidence for, such an outreach of God to humanity must therefore be the concern of the last chapter.

4

Divine Meaning and Human Becoming

> The Word of God, our Lord Jesus Christ, of [God's] boundless love, became what we are to make us what even he himself is.
>
> Irenaeus (*Adv.Haer.*, v, praef.)

In the last chapter we explored the many-levelled nature of human being which the sciences now disclose. This led me to suggest that any development of human nature, of human 'being' – any realizable process of human 'becoming' – to be truly fulfilling, nurturing and conducive to the full flourishing of humanity would need to be such as to penetrate to all those levels; and that a transformation of human being, a new actualization of human potentiality, was needed to counter the dis-ease of humanity, its inner disturbances and widely felt lack of 'fit' and harmony with its environment. Any discernment of how these needs might be satisfied involves answering two inter-locking questions.

The first is about the direction that the 'becoming' of humanity should take – what should humanity become? The second is: what *is* that 'environment 'of humanity with which it needs to be in harmony, to which it needs to be adapted? I suggested that this 'environment' extends beyond the biological, personal and social to that circumambient, creative and creating, transcendent but immanent, Reality we have named as 'God'. This indicates the need for a profound transformation of human being that would open up human existence to the transcendent God immanent in the human 'environment' in a way that would be unifying and integrating.

If God is indeed that ultimate 'environment' there would appear to be two means whereby the answers to both these questions might be forthcoming: the human search for intelligibility and meaning; and/or self-communication ('revelation') by God to humanity. The religious quest of humanity, its 'long search', may certainly minimally be regarded as constituting the first.

The religious quest

We saw that the religious consciousness of humanity has played, and still plays, a crucial role in providing individuals and societies with values and hopes that transcend their times and their commitment to their genetic kin. This 'long search' of humanity for 'God', variously named, in the major religions has been exercised with extraordinary vitality, ingenuity and richness of expression. In Western civilization we stand on a road that leads from the merger of two of the trails which started in the axial period of 800–200 BCE – those of Greece, partly transmitted via Rome, and those of ancient Israel, as transmitted and transmuted by two thousand years of Christian interpretation and expansion. This double heritage, now compounded with that scientific culture with whose impact on theology we are concerned, has shaped our consciousness. It has made us Westerners the people we are.

Hence, when we ask the crucial question of the long search, 'What can *we* know of God's meaning for humanity in this our culture?', we are compelled to recognize that, unique among the formative influences in *our* culture, and uniquely challenging in his person and teaching, there stands the figure of Jesus of Nazareth. We have been asking about the direction human 'becoming' should take. The Christian challenge is that human beings have a potentiality, not yet realized, of being in the image and likeness of God; and that the figure of Jesus Christ poses a basic initiative from God concerning the actualization of this potentiality. But – we may well ask –

Who is Jesus of Nazareth?

Those of us who are not experts have to try to find ways of steering between the Scylla of a 'biblicism' that underestimates the nature of the ancient literature from a strange culture; and the Charybdis of a scepticism that is excessive in relation to the prevailing canons of historical judgment and literary criticism of ancient sources. In this, as in life, probability must be the guide, as the redoubtable Bishop Joseph Butler long since stressed. I can but state my own position: I incline to the more 'trusting' position advocated by A. E. Harvey (1982: 4, 5):

> The Jesus who emerges from their [the writers of the Gospels] accounts has both originality and consistency . . . Unless these authors were the most consummate and imaginative artists, able to create a striking and consistent character out of scanty and unreliable sources, we have every reason to think that, in broad outline (whatever may be the case with some of the details) the Jesus whom they portray is the Jesus who actually existed. To this extent, no New Testament scholar today would be prepared to say that we can know nothing for certain about Jesus.

Historical foundations   In one of the best and most influential historical studies of this matter, *Jesus and Judaism*, E. P. Sanders (1985: 11) lists eight features, excluding sayings, about Jesus' career and its aftermath which 'can be known beyond doubt', for which 'the evidence is most secure'.

They are, roughly in chronological order:

1. Jesus was baptized by John the Baptist.
2. Jesus was a Galilean who preached and healed.
3. Jesus called disciples and spoke of there being twelve.

4. Jesus confined his activity to Israel.
5. Jesus engaged in a controversy about the temple.
6. Jesus was crucified outside Jerusalem by the Roman authorities.
7. After his death Jesus' followers continued as an identifiable movement.
8. At least some Jews persecuted at least parts of the new movement (Gal. 1.13, 22; Phil. 3.6.), and it appears that this persecution endured at least to a time near the end of Paul's career (II Cor. 11.24; Gal. 5.11; 6.12; cf. Matt. 23.34; 10.17).

There is indeed considerable convergence between various scholars on the contents of such a list.

Jesus' mission, teaching and relation to God　C.Rowland (1985: 244), in concord with innumerable other New Testament scholars, locates 'the main thrust of Jesus' message and work in the proclamation of the imminent reign of God [that is, of the kingdom of God]'. He also, with others, stresses that Jesus identifies his own presence as a sign of the initiation by God of God's imminent 'kingdom' and this *inter alia* points to Jesus having a special relationship with God which was intense and intimate – we could say that he was exceptionally 'open' to God.

Jesus: a complete human being　Since CE 451, the Definition of Chalcedon has been taken as the criterion of orthodoxy. It affirmed that Jesus was 'complete in regard to his humanity', that is, 'completely human' – indeed 'perfect' in the sense of 'complete' (Robinson, 1973: 68 and n.3) – fully human, but not necessarily displaying perfection in all conceivable human characteristics. Any assessment of Jesus must start here, along with recognizing his special vocation and relation to God.

But, one may well ask, isn't this starting point called into question by the assertion in the traditions about Jesus that there were acts of his and events associated with him that have a 'supernatural' connotation: the supposed 'miracles'?

Jesus' 'miracles'　If by a 'miracle', one means an event interpreted as not fully explicable by naturalistic means, then judgment must depend on one's *a priori* attitudes towards the very possibility of such events occurring in principle – and a scientific age is, in my view, properly sceptical. Briefly, I consider that in general the healings and apparent exorcisms give rise to no special difficulties, even for a scientific age, but that the 'nature miracles' certainly do so; and that these latter usually have features that either denote them as pure legend or as stories told with an overload of symbolic meanings – in fact, *true* 'myths'! More pertinent to our theme are the major 'miracles' connected with the person of Jesus himself.

As regards the birth of Jesus, the conclusion of the cautious – and very thorough – Roman Catholic scholar, Raymond Brown (1977: 527, emphasis in his text), is worth quoting: 'the *scientifically controllable* biblical evidence leaves the question of the historicity of the virginal conception unresolved'. This verdict would be regarded as over-cautious by other scholars: thus John Macquarrie (1990: 392–3) affirms that '. . . our historical information is negligible . . . apart from . . . scraps of doubtful information, the birth narratives [of Matthew and Luke] are manifestly legendary in character'.

Biological science, in fact, also raises acute questions about the 'virginal conception'. Since females possess only X chromosomes, conception without a father to provide a Y chromosome could lead only to a female child with two XX chromosomes – unless there was some kind of divine *de novo* creation of a Y chromosome in the ovum entering Mary's uterus, for the New Testament narratives, even if taken as historical, never deny, and indeed affirm, a normal gestation period. Even such a magical act would be beset with problems – what genes should the DNA of this Y chromosome possess? – those to give facial characteristics of Joseph, or, if not, of whom? So one can go on piling Ossa on Pelion, of one improbability on another.

But a more general consideration now weighs heavily with me because of its theological import. If Jesus is really to be fully and completely human, all that we now know scientifically about human nature shows that he must share both our evolutionary history and have the same multi-levelled basis for his person-hood – and that means he must be not only flesh of our flesh and bone of our bone, but also DNA of our DNA. If he does not, to use the traditional terms, our salvation is in jeopardy for 'what he has not assumed he has not healed' (Gregory of Nazianzus, *Ep. 101*, quoted by Bettenson 1943,1956: 64)

Hence it is *theologically* imperative that the birth stories and the doctrine of the virginal conception of Jesus be regarded in the same light as those about Adam and Eve – that is, as mythical and legendary stories intending to convey non-historical and non-biological truths. In this instance the truth being asserted is that God took the initiative in shaping and creating the person and life of Jesus of Nazareth.

The situation is quite otherwise with that other major, postu-lated 'miracle' concerning the person of Jesus – that complex of events we call his resurrection (and in which I will include also the ascension or exaltation). In the New Testament one finds (Pheme Perkins 1984)) various types of 'resurrection' affirma-tions, variously interpreted: the early kerygmatic (i.e. announc-ing) formulae and the later narratives which subdivide into those centring on the appearances of Jesus to his disciples and other, even later ones, on the finding of the empty tomb.

It is not at all clear that the narratives of the 'resurrection', taken at their face value, are sensitive to scientific considerations at all, since the end state, the 'risen' Jesus, is not open even to the *kind* of repeatable observations science involves. The only science which might have any direct bearing by its very nature on the evidence of the disciples' experience of the risen Jesus is that of psychology. But the probability that these diverse experiences of different kinds of people were due to a kind of communal hallucination or psychosis is minimal in the light of the variety of these same witnesses. Furthermore, this judgment is supported by their willingness, and of those to whom they communicated their experiences, to suffer and die for their belief.

The evidence is that this was a genuine experience within the consciousness of these witnesses. Such a complex of psychological experiences, especially when they are communal, would well manifest a new reality only discernible in that particular complex combination. For the concept of 'resurrection' appears not to be reducible to any purely psychological account and the affirmations of the New Testament that propose it can properly be claimed to be referring to a new kind of reality, hitherto unknown because not hitherto experienced – and on which the sciences as such can make no comment. I recall the penetrating statement of Christopher Evans (1983):

> The core of resurrection faith is that already within the temporal order of existence a new beginning of life from God, and a living of life under God, are possible, and are anticipatory of what human life has it in it to be as divine creation; and that this has been made apprehensible and available in the life and death of Christ regarded both as divine illumination of human life and as effective power for overcoming whatever obstructs it.

'*Who do you say I am?*' was the question that the Synoptic Gospels report (Mark 8.27–33 parallels) as being addressed by Jesus to his disciples at Caesarea Philippi at a crucial point in his ministry. We have been setting out, as it were, some of the pieces of the jigsaw of what we know about Jesus historically. Even when we have had to abandon the more 'super-naturalist' features in the Gospel accounts of Jesus and in the general past traditions of the Christian church – for the most part pre-scientific and pre-critical – we can nevertheless understand how these stories became attached to someone whose spiritual quality and power made such a very great impact, and still does. This apprehension of the compellingly attractive nature of Jesus' life, teaching and death (and even resurrection) is not confined to Christians. He certainly bestrides the world religions 'like a Colossus'. His presence in history constitutes a turning point in that long search of humanity for God. Its distinctive challenge to us, as for his first disciples, is that he evokes in us a sense, less that in him we find a path *to* God, but rather that in him we encounter a self-communication *from* God to us – and above all in the resurrection experienced by his disciples.

We now have to examine if the pieces of the jigsaw can in fact be assembled today by means of some kind of framework to allow us to discern a coherent pattern which, by being such a self-communication of God to humanity, could also be a clue to the answer to our earlier question concerning what human beings should be becoming. Such a framework, I am suggesting, is provided by those apprehensions of natural and divine being and becoming which have been earlier developed as credible in the light of our scientific insights into the nature and history of the world.

'The Jesus of history and the Christ of faith'

New Testament scholars have uncovered a rich treasury of ways in which the impact of Jesus on his first disciples was interpreted; and it transpires that what the New Testament gives us is not so much an intellectual synthesis as a kaleidoscopic variety of poetic insights.

Much of the intensive debate about how to formulate Jesus' relation to God and to the rest of humanity has been confused, in my view, by not being based on an intelligible and believable account of the issues we have been dealing with in these pages. It is in this contemporary theological framework so constructed that we now have to re-consider the 'things about Jesus' in order to formulate what significance Jesus could have for us today. Is the concept of the 'incarnation', which emerged towards the end of the first century CE, intelligible enough in *this* framework still to be credible today as a justifiable interpretation of those 'things about Jesus' which have a historical basis? The meanings which God can express in his creation and in human history are relative to the receptiveness and outlook, the interpretative horizons, of those to whom he is communicating. We still have to ask about Jesus, following L. Hodgson (1956: x): 'What must the truth have been and be if that is how it looked to people [e.g., 'John'] who thought and wrote like that?'

How could God communicate through Jesus?

God's interaction with the world has earlier been characterized as a holistic, whole-part, continuing process of input of 'information', whereby God's meanings and purposes are implemented in the shaping of particular events, or patterns of events, without any abrogation of the regularities discerned by the sciences in the natural order. Amongst the constituents of that world are human beings who are persons. These too can be 'informed' by God through the nexus of events, which includes events in human-brains-in-human-bodies.

How, in the light of this, might we then interpret the experience of God that was mediated to his disciples and to the New Testament church through Jesus? We need to explicate in these terms the conclusions of scholars about the understanding in New Testament times of Jesus the Christ – as represented, for example, by J. D. G. Dunn (1980: his emphasis):

> Initially Christ was thought of . . . as *the climactic embodiment of God's power and purpose . . . God himself reaching out to men . . . God's creative wisdom . . . God's revelatory word . . . God's clearest self-expression, God's last word.*

Such descriptions of what Jesus the Christ was to those who encountered him and to the early church are all, in their various ways, about God *communicating* to humanity, and so, in the broad sense we have been using the terms, about an 'input of information' from God, which we earlier also denoted as the conveying of 'meaning' from God to humanity through events and patterns of events in the created world. The early witnesses experienced in Jesus, in his very person and personal history, a communication *from God*, a revelation of God's meanings for humanity. So it is no wonder that, in order to say what meaning Jesus the Christ had for him and the church, the author named John at a later stage of reflection in the New Testament period, in the Prologue to the Fourth Gospel conflated a number of available concepts into that of Jesus as the *Word* of God, the *Logos* of God, in a human being.

Now the conveying of meaning, in the ordinary sense, is implemented initially by an input of 'information' – the constrained and selected elements among all possibilities that sufficiently delimit signals (i.e., language and other means of human communication) so that they can convey meaning.

The use of the concept of 'information input' to refer to the way God induces effects in the world was, as far as I know, pioneered by John Bowker (1978: 187–8):

> . . . it is credibly and conceptually possible to regard Jesus as a wholly God-informed person, who retrieved the theistic inputs coded in . . . brain-processes for the scan of every situation, and for every utterance, verbal and non-verbal . . . It is possible on this basis to talk about a wholly human figure, without loss or compromise, and to talk also, at exactly the same moment, of a wholly real presence of God so far as that [divine] nature . . . can be mediated to and through . . . through the process of brain behaviour by which any human being becomes an informed subject – but in this case, perhaps even uniquely, a wholly God-informed subject.'

At this juncture in our enterprise, recognition that God has, in fact, communicated God's own self to humanity in this way –

that is, acceptance of the belief, given its intelligibility, that God was in this sense 'incarnate' in Jesus – is, of course, a matter of individual judgment. Here we shall continue to explore its implications because one of the criteria of a sound hypothesis is that it should prove fruitful and illuminating. So we go on to ask what was it that God may actually be said to have communicated to humanity about God's own self in and through Jesus the Christ, said to be the 'Word made flesh'?

God's self-expression in Jesus the Christ

God as continuous and immanent Creator That qualitatively new kinds of existence come into being is one of the most striking aspects of natural becoming – we witness the seeming paradox of discontinuity generated by continuity. Earlier this feature of the world was associated with God as continuously creating, as the immanent Creator, in and through the natural order. Hence when we reflect on the significance of what the early witnesses reported as their experience of Jesus the Christ, we find ourselves emphasizing both the *continuity* of Jesus with the rest of humanity, and so with the rest of nature within which humanity evolved; and, at the same time, emphasizing also the *discontinuity* constituted by what is distinctive in his relation to God and what through him (his teaching, life, death and resurrection) the early witnesses experienced *of* God. This prompts an understanding of what is traditionally known as the 'incarnation' that occurred in Jesus as exemplifying uniquely that emergence-from-continuity which characterizes the whole process whereby God is informing the world and creating continuously through discontinuity. That is, in the light of our understanding of God's creation and presence in the world, we can now interpret 'incarnation' not as involving any 'descent' into the world of God conceived of as 'above' (and so outside) it – as so many Christmas hymns would have us believe – but as the manifestation of what, or rather the One who, is already in the world but not recognized or known (which is what the first chapter of John's Gospel actually says). The human person Jesus is then to be seen, by virtue of his human response and openness to God, as the locus, the *ikon*, in and through whom there is made open and explicit the nature and character of the God who has never ceased to be present continuously creating and bringing God's purposes to fruition in the order of energy-matter-space-time. We have to come to see Jesus the Christ as the distinctive manifestation of a possibility always inherently there for human beings by virtue of their potential nature. This makes what he *was* relevant to what we *might* be. For it entails that what we have affirmed about Jesus is not, in principle, impossible for all humanity – even if, as a matter of contingent historical fact, we think that manifest 'incarnation' is only fully to be seen in him, it is not excluded as a possibility for all humanity. Jesus is the human person God actually became and a new mode of human being appeared.

God as personal and purposive   We have noted that the operation of natural selection in biological organisms has an inbuilt tendency to favour, because of their survival-value, increasing complexity, information-processing and -storage ability – the very foundations for human personhood. This seemed to justify tentatively the description of the universe as a 'personalizing universe', in the sense of John Robinson (1967: 97) that 'the whole is to be understood as a process making for personality and beyond'.

Meanings which persons wish to communicate are conveyed through words and the concept of the Word/*Logos* of God is therefore an essentially personal one. Thus what God communicated to humanity about God's own self in Jesus the Christ has made explicit that significance of personhood in the divine purposes which was only partially and incompletely discernible in natural being and becoming. This also compels the recognition that it is the eliciting of persons embodying *values* which is the underlying purpose of the divine creative process, for it was a life of a *particular* kind, instantiating values based on self-offering love, that we see in Jesus the Christ. So, in this sense, the 'incarnation' which occurred in Jesus the Christ may then properly be said to be the consummation of the creative and creating evolutionary process; that is, the evoking in the created world of the kind of personhood manifest in him, with his particular embodiment of values, is unveiled as the purpose of God in creation.

Furthermore, as regards God's revelation of God's own self, we can now say that, because in the human person of Jesus the Christ God has been able to self-express God's own self, the attribution to God of personal language is thereby further justified even as we recognize its inherent limitations.

God as exploring in creation through its open-endedness   Our earlier recognition, in the first chapter, that God as Creator acts through chance operating under the constraints of law and that many of the processes of the world are open-ended (they are irreducibly unpredictable and some are inherently so), together with a renewed emphasis on the immanence of God in the creative and creating processes of the world, led us to suggest that it was legitimate to speak of God the Creator as *exploring* in creation. This is the notion that God improvisingly responds to and creates on the basis of eventualities which are often inherently unpredictable in advance, such as the operations of human free will.

Jesus, a complete human being, exercised his free will to be entirely open to God to such a distinctive degree that his disciples came to designate him as the 'Christ' – the 'Anointed by God' – and their successors to develop an understanding of what was happening in him as the 'incarnation' of God, God's very self-expression, or embodiment, in a human person. This means that, in Jesus the Christ, the open-endedness of what is going on in the world, self-consciously and overtly by the willing act of a created human being was united with the purposes of God for the still open future, and so with the immanent activity of God who is the source of the world's open future.

But is not this just that very close linkage between the advent of Jesus and the initiation of the Kingdom of God ('God's Reign') which is so well testified as distinctive of Jesus' own teaching? Jesus the Christ can be seen as a new departure point in the creative, innovatory, exploration of God in God's own creation.

God as 'self-limited' and as vulnerable, self-emptying, self-giving, and suffering Love In the first chapter, 'self-limitation' was attributed to God with respect to God's own power over all events and knowledge of the future. Now, if Jesus the Christ is the self-expression of God in a human person, this inevitably involves a self-limitation of God with respect to God's power and knowledge. The self-expression of God, in 'the fullness of time', in the restricted human personhood of Jesus can therefore be regarded as an explicit manifestation and revelation of that perennial (self-limiting, -emptying, -giving) relation of God to the created world which was up till then only implicit and hidden.

Earlier, God was also said to be, as it were, 'taking a risk' in creating and therein making Godself and God's purposes vulnerable to the inherent open-endedness of the creative interplay of chance and law. This aspect of God's creative work is overtly communicated by God, if God truly self-expressed Godself in Jesus the Christ, whose path through life was preeminently one of vulnerability to the forces that swirled around him, to which he eventually innocently succumbed in acute suffering and, from his human perception, in a tragic, abandoned death.

Because sacrificial, self-limiting, self-giving action on behalf of the good of others is, in human life, the hallmark of love, those who believe in Jesus the Christ as the self-expression of God's own self have come to see his life as their ultimate warrant for asserting that God is essentially 'Love', in so far as any one word can accurately refer to God's nature. It has already also been tentatively inferred, from the character of the natural processes of creation, that God could be regarded as suffering in, with and under these selfsame processes with their costly, open-ended unfolding in time. But if God was indeed present in and one with Jesus the Christ, then we have to conclude that *God* also suffered in and with him in his passion and death. The tragedy of Jesus' actual human life can be seen as a drawing back of the curtain to unveil a God suffering in and with the sufferings of created humanity and so, by a natural extension, with those of all creation, since humanity is an evolved part of it. In Jesus the Christ, the suffering of God is concentrated into a point of intensity and transparency which reveals it to all who focus on him.

Belief in Jesus the Christ as the self-expression of God in the confines of a human person is therefore entirely consonant with that conception of God which affirms that God, in exercising divine creativity, is self-limiting, vulnerable, self-emptying and self-giving suffering Love – supremely Love in creative action. On this understanding Jesus the Christ is the definitive communication from God to humanity of the deep meaning of what God has been effecting all along in creation.

But what the disciples and their followers experienced in Jesus the Christ, as interpreted by them and down the centuries by the church, also has immense significance for our perceptions of *human* potentialities and to these we must now turn.

The divine meaning of created human being

In the previous chapter human beings were seen to consist of and operate at various levels which are the foci of the different sciences and that these levels merge into that of human culture and its products. The uniqueness of this comprehensive unity-in-diversity and diversity-in-unity that is a human being was encapsulated in our use of the term 'person' as denoting both the integrated sum, as it were, over all these discriminable levels and that elusive, mysterious almost, nature of the whole. The Christian affirmation is, we are suggesting, that God totally 'informed' the human person of Jesus at all levels of his created humanity and this 'informing' was coincidental and co-ordinate *pari passu* with his total and personal human response of openness and obedience to God his 'Father'. In this way, Jesus the Christ throws new light on the divine meaning of the multiple levels of the created world which were present in him and most of which came into existence in evolution before the species, *homo sapiens*, to which he himself belonged. For the significance and potentiality of all levels of creation may be said to have been unfolded in Jesus the Christ. In his relation as a created human person to God the Creator he mediates to us the *meaning* of creation – we learn through him that for which all things were made, how God has been shaping creation for the emergence of persons in communion with Godself. For the meaning which God communicates through Jesus the Christ, through the Christ-event, is the meaning of God both *about* humanity as well as *for* humanity. The meaning he (Jesus) discerns, proclaims, expresses and reveals is the meaning that he himself *is*.

Jesus the Christ may then be seen as a specific, indeed for Christians a unique, focal point in which the diverse meanings written into the many levels of creation coalesce like rays of light with an intensity that so illuminates for us the purposes of God that we are better able to interpret God's meanings communicated in his creative activity over a wider range of human experience of nature and history. This perception of 'incarnation' is well-expressed by John Macquarrie (1990: 392):

> . . . incarnation was not a sudden once-for-all-event . . . but is a process which began with the creation . . . 'incarnation' . . . is the progressive presencing and self-manifestation of the Logos in the physical and historical world. For the Christian, this process reaches its climax in Jesus Christ . . . the

difference between Christ and other agents of the Logos is one of degree, not of kind.

What Jesus the Christ was and what happened to him can, in this perspective, be seen as a new source and resource for reading God's meaning for humanity in all the levels of creation leading to and incorporated into humanity – the clue that points us to a meaning beyond itself, a key that unlocks the door on to a more ample vista, a focus of rays coming from many directions, a characteristic gesture from the hand of God revealing God's meaning and purpose and nature.

The divine meaning for human becoming

We have had to recognize the paradoxical character of our 'as yet unfinished humanity' and our need to discern what we *ought* to be and be becoming. So we have now to ask, if 'God was in Christ', what does the Christ event tell us about God's ultimate purposes for human nature, for human becoming – that is, for the realization of human potential, for human fulfilment, flourishing and even consummation?

Historical evidence could never prove the negative proposition that Jesus was 'sinless', even if that which is available were much more ample than it actually is in the four Gospels. What is distinctive about Jesus was his openness to and intimacy with God his Father and his complete self-offering obedience to the will of God to the point of his ultimate surrender to, and acceptance of, death by crucifixion; and that the experience of his disciples caused them to believe that, after his very real death, his life – *his* particular life of *that* particular kind – had been taken in its full identity and personhood through death 'up' into the very Being of God. It was this which generated the conviction that he had an ultimate significance as a window into, an *ikon* of, God's own nature and as revealing what humanity

was meant by God to become – namely, united to God in
self-offering love for God and others. Jesus' resurrection
demonstrated to them, notably to Paul, and now to us, that it is
the union of *his* kind of life with God which is not broken by
death and capable of being taken up into God. For he manifested
the kind of human life which can become fully life with God, not
only here and now, but eternally beyond the threshold of death.
Hence his imperative 'Follow me' now constitutes for us a call
for the transformation of humanity into a new kind of human
being – and becoming. Clearly what happened to him, Jesus saw
could happen to all.

In this perspective, Jesus the Christ, the whole Christ event,
has shown us what is possible for humanity. The actualization of
this potentiality can properly be regarded as the consummation
of the purposes of God in the evolution of humanity. To become
one with God, to be fully open to God in self-offering love,
is now to be perceived as the ultimate realization of human
potential. Hence Jesus the Christ occupies in 'spiritual' history
(that is, the history of the relationship of humanity with God)
the place that a mutation does in biological evolution – an
irreversible transformation into a new kind of existence allowing
the actualization of new possibilities. In this sense, all humanity
can aspire to becoming 'Christlike' and can hope, as Paul puts it
(Gal. 4.19 NEB/REB), to 'take the shape/form of Christ'. It
was an act of new *creation* because the initiative was from God
within human history, within the responsive human will of Jesus
inspired by that outreach of God into humanity traditionally
designated as 'God the Holy Spirit'. Jesus the Christ is thereby
seen, in the context of the whole Christ event, as the model of
what God intends for all human beings now revealed as having
the potentiality of responding to, being open to, of becoming one
with, God.

The divine initiative in human becoming

But how can what happened in and to him, there and then, happen in us, here and now? Can what happened in and to him be effectual, some two thousand years later, in a way that might actually enable us to live in harmony with God, ourselves and our fellow human beings – that is, experience the fulfilment for which human nature yearns? Any answer will have to be grounded on our sharing a common humanity with this Jesus and, furthermore, there are certain features in scientific perspectives which constrain a response today, namely:

1. Biological death of the individual, as the means of the evolutionary creation of new species by natural selection, cannot now be attributed to human 'sin';
2. The evidence is all against human beings ever in the past having been in some golden age of innocence and perfection from which they have 'fallen'.

'God was in Christ reconciling the world to himself', St Paul attested (II Cor. 5.19 REB) and the working out of how this might be so has been historically the intention of theories of the 'atonement', the 'at-one-ment', often also referred to as the 'work of Christ'. The Nicene Creed simply affirms baldly that Christ 'was crucified *for us* under Pontius Pilate. He suffered and was buried'. This reticent 'for us' encompasses a very wide range of interpretations. Although the church in its many branches has never officially endorsed any one particular theory of this claimed atonement, yet a number have become widely disseminated doctrinally, liturgically and devotionally. These purportedly 'objective' theories of the atonement rely heavily on pre-suppositions about death and the 'Fall', just mentioned as called into question in the light of well-founded science. They also fail to incorporate our sense derived from the vista of evolution unfolded by the sciences of humanity as *emerging* into individual and corporate consciousness and self-consciousness, awareness of values, social co-operation, human culture; and into a sense of and awareness of God.

The classical theories of the atonement fail to express any dynamic sense of the process of human *becoming* as still going on. They also fail to make clear how the human response which is an essential part of the reconciliation between God and humanity is evoked.

So the question can now be put as: How can what happened in and to Jesus the Christ actually evoke in us the response that is needed for our reconciliation to God and actually enable us to live in harmony with God and humanity here and now?

This question may be answered most effectively, it seems to me, by seeing the life, suffering and death of Jesus the Christ as an *act of love*, an act of love *of God*, an act of love *by God*.

In the suffering and death of Jesus the Christ, we now also concomitantly perceive and experience the suffering, self-offering love of God in action, no more as abstract knowledge, as might well have been the case in our previous reflections on God as Creator suffering in, with and under creation. For we have recognized that the openness and obedience of the human Jesus to God enabled him, as *the* God-informed human person, to be a manifest self-expression in history, in the confines of human personhood, of God as creative, self-expressive, Word/*Logos*/ 'Son'. In and with the suffering and cross of Jesus the Christ we witness *God* explicitly in history undergoing that suffering which God's vulnerable, self-offering Love eternally invests in his work of ongoing creation, with all the self-limitation that that involves. In his humanly experienced anguish, we see *God* going to the ultimate in suffering love on behalf of humanity, in an act of Love 'for us'. Thereby is uniquely and definitively revealed the depths of the divine Love for humanity and the cost of God's gracious outreach to us as we are, alienated from God, humanity and ourselves, that is, as 'sinners'. As such this love of God engages us, where 'to engage' means (*Oxford English Dictionary*): 'to attract and hold fast; to involve; to lay under obligation; to urge, induce; to gain, win over.' The cross is a proposal of God's love and *as such* engages our response. Once we have really come to know that it was God's love in action 'for us' in the Christ event, then we can never be the same again. God in that outreach to humanity, we denote as God the Holy Spirit, united the human Jesus with the Father, his Creator, and can now kindle and generate in us a love for God our Creator and for the humanity for whom Jesus died, as we contemplate God in Christ on the cross.

What is being proposed here is that this action of God as Holy Spirit in us, in engaging our response, is itself effecting our at-one-ment, is effecting our 'salvation', actually bringing us into harmony with God, making us whole, making us 'holier'. That is, it is 'salvific'. For thereby we are enabled to share in Jesus Christ's own life of obedience towards his and our Father, of becoming open to God in the way he himself was and consti-tutes our at-one-ment with God, with our fellow human beings and with ourselves. It is a path costly to God and costly to us.

This conceiving of the 'work of Christ', as achieving of at-one-ment through the Christ event, as an act of and engage-ment with us of God's suffering, self-offered Love coheres with our present evolutionary perceptions that the specifically human emerged and still emerges only gradually and fitfully in human history, without a historic 'Fall'.

Furthermore, since God took Jesus through death into his own life, there is implied in the initiation and continuation of this process in us, that we too can thereby be taken up into the life of God, can be 'resurrected' in some way akin to that of Jesus the Christ. Since Jesus was apprehended as having been taken through death with his personhood and identity intact and as having been 'taken up' into the presence of God, it *could* happen to us and that is the ground of our hope for our individual future and that of humanity corporately. The virtue of being agnostic about the relation between the empty tomb and the risen Christ here becomes apparent. For, within a relatively short time after our own biological death, our bodies will lose their identity as their atomic and molecular constituents begin to disperse through the earth and its atmosphere, often becoming part of other human beings.

Furthermore the interpretation of the death and resurrection of Jesus as manifesting uniquely the quality of life which can be taken up by God into the fullness of God's own life implicitly involves an affirmation about what the basic potentiality of all humanity is. It shows us that, regardless of our particular human skills and creativities – indeed regardless of almost all that the social mores of our times applauds – it is through a radical open-ness to God, a thoroughgoing self-offering love for others and obedience to God that we grow into such communion with the eternal God that *God* does not allow biological death to rupture that essentially timeless relation.

Postscript

In this work, I have been trying to sketch out a theology which is both rooted in the Judaeo-Christian tradition and also consonant and coherent with those scientific perspectives on the world which are well-established enough in our culture to form the pre-suppositions of most of our thinking, at least in the 'West'. The result is, I would hope, a reasonable locating and exposition of the basic essentials of the Christian revelation within that context of a world profoundly influenced by and indebted to the perspectives of the sciences. It has been my hope that this approach might encourage genuine inquirers to take with utter seriousness at least the putative reasonableness of the claim that in Jesus the Christ there has been a revelation in incarnation of the God who is eternally the transcendent-immanent Creator whose fundamental nature is best described as that of Love. And that such unprejudiced inquirers might, furthermore, come to see that Jesus the Christ is the consummation both of the creative work of God in evolution and of the revelation of God made to the people of Israel; that in and through him human beings can receive insight into the potentialities of their own being and becoming; that through their response to the revelation of God as Love, made explicit in the Christ event, God can also effect in them a re-orientation of their self-understanding and a transformation of their relation to God; and that thereby they can begin to become what God intended them to be and become, namely, one with God, in harmony with God's own self and purposes in the world and with their fellow human beings and nature.

In these last sections of this concluding chapter, our experience of God was very readily expressible implicitly in the language of the so-called 'economic' Trinity, the manifestation for humanity of God's Being and Becoming in the world; *from* God as Father, *through* God as Word/*Logos*/Son, *in* God as Holy Spirit. How – indeed, whether or not – this threefold experience of God in God's creative and salvific outreach to the world is related to any differentiation within God's inner being and becoming (the so-called 'essential' Trinity) is still a matter for much hard thinking and clarification. For there is indeed, as pointed out in the first chapter, an ineffable richness, analogous to that of personal communion, within the divine life, a diversity within a fundamental unity, that escapes precise articulation.

It is related (Copleston 1955: 10) that one of the greatest theologians of the Christian era, St Thomas Aquinas, suspended work on the third part of his great *Summa Theologiae*, telling his secretary that, after an experience while saying Mass in December 1273, he would write no more for, he said, 'All that I have written seems to me like so much straw compared with what I have seen and with what has been revealed to me.' Theology which is not fed by and consummated in prayer and worship is indeed sterile and can deteriorate into a merely intellectual exercise. Who, writing or speaking on the profundity that is God, cannot but feel with St Thomas that the bricks of his or her constructions are made only of straw? Nevertheless, we are commanded to love God with our minds and so such an enterprise as this is worthwhile if its limitations are recognized – that talk about God, theo-logy, is but ancillary to prayer, worship and action. But to pray and to worship and to act we need supportable and believable models and images of the One to whom prayer, worship and action are to be directed. This work is offered as a necessarily inadequate contribution to that pressing and perennial task of refurbishing our images of God – and of humanity.

Reference Bibliography

Abrahamsen, A. A.
  1987: 'Bridging Boundaries versus Breaking Boundaries: Psycho-linguistics in Perspective', *Synthese* 72

Bechtel, W. S. and Abrahamsen, A. A
  1990: *Connectionism and the Mind: An Introduction to Parallel Processing in Networks* (Oxford: Blackwell)
Bettenson, H.
  1943, 1956: *Documents of the Christian Church* (London: Oxford University Press)
Bowker, John
  1978: *Religious Imagination and the Sense of God* (Oxford: Clarendon Press)
Brooke, J. H.
  1991: *Science and Religion: Some Historical Perspectives* (Cambridge: Cambridge University Press)
Broughton, R.
  1992: *Parapsychology: The Controversial Science* (London: Rider)
Brown, D.
  1985: *The Divine Trinity* (London: Duckworth)
  1990: 'God and Symbolic Action', in *Divine Action: Studies Inspired by the Philosophical Theology of Austin Farrer*, ed. B. Hebblethwaite and E. Henderson (Edinburgh: T. & T. Clark)
Brown, R.E.
  1977: *The Birth of the Messiah* (London: Chapman)

Campbell, D.T.
  1974: ' "Downward Causation" in Hierarchically Organised Systems', in *Studies in the Philosophy of Biology: Reductionism and Related Problems*, ed. F. J. Ayala, and T. Dobzhansky, (London: Macmillan) 179–186
Churchland, P. S. and Sejnowski, T. J.

1988: 'Perspectives on Cognitive Neuroscience', *Science* 242
Copleston, F. C.
  1955: *Aquinas* (London: Penguin Books)
Crutchfield, J. P. et al.
  1986: 'Chaos', *Scientific American,* 38–49

Dunn, J. D. G.
  1980: *Christology in the Making* (London; SCM Press; Philadelphia: Westminster Press)

Eaves, L. J. and Gross, L. M.
  1990: 'Theological Reflections on the Cultural Impact of Human Genetics', *Insights,* 2 (Chicago Center for Religion and Science)
Eigen, M. and Winkler, R.
  1981: *Laws of the Game* (London: Allen Lane; New York: Knopf)
Evans, C. F.
  1983: 'Resurrection', in *A New Dictionary of Christian Theology,* ed. A. Richardson and J. Bowden (London: SCM Press; Philadelphia: Westminster Press)

Gould, S. J.
  1989: *Wonderful Life: the Burgess Shale and the Nature of History* (New York: Norton)

Hardy, A.
  1979: *The Spiritual Nature of Man* (Oxford: Clarendon Press)
Harvey, A. E.
  1982: *Jesus and the Constraints of History* (London: Duckworth)
Hay, D. A.
  1985: *Essentials of Behaviour Genetics* (Oxford: Blackwell)
Hay, David
  1990: *Religious Experience Today: Studying the Facts* (London: Mowbray)
Hodgson, L.
  1956: *For Faith and Freedom* (Oxford: Oxford University Press)
Hoyle, F.
  1960: *The Nature of the Universe* (Oxford: Blackwell)
Jantzen, G.
  1987: 'Conspicuous Sanctity and Religious Belief', in *The Rationality of Religious Belief,* ed. W. J. Abraham, and S. W. Holzer, (Oxford: Clarendon Press)

Jeeves, M. A.

   1991: 'Minds and Brains: Then and Now', *Interdisciplinary Science Reviews* 16

Jenkins, D.

   1987: *God, Miracle and the Church of England* (London: SCM Press)

Lucas, J. R.

   1979: 'Wilberforce and Huxley: A Legendary Encounter', *Historical Journal* 22 (2), 313–330

Macquarrie, J.

   1982: *In Search of Humanity: A Theological and Philosophical Approach* (London: SCM Press; New York: Crossroad)

   1987: 'A Theology of Personal Being', in A. R. Peacocke, and G. Gillett, (eds), *Persons and Personality* (Oxford: Blackwell)

   1990: *Jesus Christ in Modern Thought* (London: SCM Press; Philadelphia: Trinity Press International)

McMullin, E.

   1984: 'The Case for Scientific Realism', in *Scientific Realism* ed. J. Leplin (Berkeley and Los Angeles: University of California Press)

Morea, P.

   1990: *Personality: An Introduction to the Theories of Psychology* (Harmondsworth: Penguin Books)

Pailin, D.

   1983: 'Revelation', in *A New Dictionary of Christain Theology*, ed. A. Richardson and J. Bowden, (London: SCM Press; Philadelphia: Westminster), 504–506)

Peacocke, A. R.

   1983, reprinted 1989: *An Introduction to the Physical Chemistry of Biological Organization* (Oxford: Clarendon Press)

   1993: *Theology for a Scientific Age: Being and Becoming – Natural, Divine and Human*, second enlarged edition (London: SCM Press; Minneapolis: Fortress)

Perkins, P.

   1984: *Resurrection: New Testament Witness and Contemporary Reflection* (London: Chapman)

Prigogine, I.

   1980: *From Being to Becoming* (San Francisco: Freeman)

Prigogine, I. and Stengers, I.
  1984: *Order out of Chaos: Man's Dialogue with Nature* (London: Heinemann)
Quick, O.
  1927 [1955]: *The Christian Sacraments* (London: Nisbet)

Richardson, A.
  1957: 'Adam, Man', in *A Theological Wordbook of the Bible*, ed. A. Richardson (London: SCM Press)
Robinson, John A. T.
  1967: *Exploration into God* (London: SCM Press)
  1973: *The Human Face of God* (London: SCM Press)
Rolston, H.
  1967: *Science and Religion: A Critical Survey* (New York: Random House)
Rowland, C.
  1985: *Christian Origins* (London: SPCK)

Sanders, E. P.
  1985: *Jesus and Judaism* (London: SCM Press; Philadelphia: Fortress)
Sayers, D.
  1949: English translation, with introduction and notes, of Dante's *Divine Comedy: Hell*
Sayers, D. and Reynolds, B.
  1962: English translation, with introduction and notes, of Dante's *Divine Comedy: Paradise*
Sperry, R. W.
  1983: *Science and Moral Priority* (Oxford: Blackwell)
  1988: 'Psychology's Mentalist Paradigm and the Religion/Science Tension' *American Psychologist* 43
Steiner, G.
  1989: *Real Presences* (London: Faber & Faber)
Swinburne, R.
  1979: *The Existence of God* (Oxford: Clarendon Press)
Temple. W.
  1931: *Thoughts on Some Problems of the Day* (London: Macmillan)
Vale, J. R.
  1973: *American Psychologist*, 28
Williams, R.
  1986: 'Trinity and Revelation', *Modern Theology* 2, 200

Index